OPERATION:
MILITARY RESOURCES
VOLUME 2

KIMBERLY SUCHEK

10% of each book sold is donated to <u>VetBiz of Michigan</u> which assists veterans with starting and expanding their own businesses when they leave the military.

Operation: Military Resources Volume II
© 2015 Kimberly Suchek
Published in 2015 by Creative Freedom, LLC

ISBN:
Print: 978-0-9847284-4-2
Kindle: 978-0-9847284-5-9
epub: 978-0-9847284-6-6
iTunes: 978-0-9847284-7-3

You may reach the author at Kim@MilitaryResourceBooks.com

Photo credits the US Armed Forces, the Veterans Administration, the VFW Headquarters for the State of Michigan, Our Military Kids, Alane Pearce. Photographs used with permission. Some photographs are in public domain.

Editing, Layout and design by Alane Pearce Professional Writing Services. Contact at MyPublishingCoach.com.

Suchek, Kimberly: OPERATION: MILITARY RESOURCES
1. Resource   2. Military Life   3. Nonfiction

What People Are Saying About Operation: Military Resources Vol 2

A very well executed book regarding military resources! A great deal of effort, organization, and care has gone into this easily formatted book to better help veterans, their families, and advocates identify the right resource. Bravo!

Elena Bridges
Military Spouse
Chairperson, West Michigan Veterans Coalition
Veterans Services Community Coordinator, Altarum Institute

It is my opinion that this book of resources is a gold mine for every military veteran and their family.

Our heroes of this country have many needs after they come back from their military service for the betterment of their health and the welfare of their family.

There is no greater incentive that we as Americans can have than to see the smiles on our military families faces when we help them. Kim is being a tremendous help and a shining and guiding light to lead them thru life with her book.

I am extremely proud of Kim and proud to call her friend for writing this book to bring hope, faith and great expectations to our veterans who are in need.

Carl A. Cronk Jr.
Army Ambassador
Veteran's Service Officer
Retired Army
Vietnam Veteran And Very Proud American

What can one say about this masterful, detailed in depth comprehensive resource that identifies virtually anything and everything of value and need for the military family? It is the ultimate short cut to finding immediate solutions and answers. It's a must acquisition. Don't leave home without it!

Woodrow D. Wollesen
Army Veteran, Author, Serial Entrepreneur, Founder - Operation Veteran Empowerment

This book is a must-have for any active duty personal or veteran that has left the service. This book goes far beyond your typical military benefits and provides the reader with a wealth of information on Education, health, military families., discounts for veterans and much more.

As an Army veteran I do not hesitate to endorse this book and I encourage everyone to have a copy it,

Matt Sherwood-Executive Director
VetBizCentral
810-767-8387 fax 810-767-8662
www.vetbizcentral.org
skype @ matt.sherwood10

I am excited about the release of this book. The first volume blessed me and my family and I am confident this one will too. This book includes a wealth of knowledge which benefits soldiers, spouses, and dependents. As a military spouse and parent, it is often difficult to find a multitude of resources in one location. Mrs. Kim Suchek did an awesome job making my search easier. There are many resources in this book I didn't know existed. Due to Mrs. Suchek's tremendous efforts organizing her book, I found resources about relaxation facilities for my husband and I as well as military scholarships available for my daughters who are attending college. I love this book and you will too!

Mrs. Doreatha Rusher
A military spouse and mother

Praise for OPERATION: MILITARY RESOURCES VOL 1

I strongly applaud the motivation behind this book. With hundreds of thousands of young men and women cycling through the armed forces, we need a good resource that tells them what to expect from the military in the way of services and what other services they can take advantage of. All in all, a lot of good information.

**Writer's Digest Self Published Book Awards
Contest Judge**

This book is a great resource for military personnel and their families. It contains thorough, well curated and annotated lists of resources and resource providers. While the author's approach is intensely practical, it's also rooted in her deep compassion for the men and women of the military and their families. Many of the resources are military specific, and some are for specific branches of the military, but some of the resources are even helpful for families outside the military. The type setting is easy to read, and the side tabs on the pages make it simple to find exactly what you're looking for.

***Writer's Digest Self Published Book Awards
Contest Judge***

I GOT YOUR BACK

By Autumn Parker

I am a small and precious child, my dad's been sent to fight...
The only place I'll see his face, is in my dreams at night.
He will be gone too many days for my young mind to keep track.
I may be sad, but I am proud.
My daddy's got your back.

I am a caring mother; my son has gone to war...
My mind is filled with worries that I have never known before.
Every day I try to keep my thoughts from turning black.
I may be scared, but I am proud.
My son has got your back.

I am a strong and loving wife, with a husband soon to go.
There are times I'm terrified, in a way most never know.
I bite my lip, and force a smile, as I watch my husband pack....
My heart may break, but I am proud.
My husband's got your back...

I am a soldier...
Serving proudly, standing tall.
I fight for freedom, yours and mine, by answering this call.
I do my job while knowing, the thanks it sometimes lacks.
Say a prayer that I'll come home.
It's me who's got your back.

*This poem is used by written permission
from the author, Autumn Parker*

DEDICATION

For my Grandma Joe Joe
and my family,
thank you for your faith in me

For our service members and their families who
serve and sacrifice for our country,
thank you!

ABOUT THE AUTHOR

Kimberly Suchek is passionate about quality of life issues for military families. She has been married to an Army National Guard Soldier for over 16 years and lives and understands the many challenges the military lifestyle presents before, during and after deployments; she is concerned that military families do not know about all the programs and organizations there are to help during the different transitions of military life.

Kimberly is a freelance writer, Weekly Column Writer for Stars & Stripes and a published author. She is also past President of Operation Homefront of Michigan, Family Assistant Coordinator for the Army nation Guard out of Joint Force HQ and Grand Ledge Armory and a DEERS Operator. She was also a patrol officer for six years. Although she holds an Associate Degree in Criminal Justice, she hopes to go back to school and finish her Bachelor's Degree. Kim loves being outdoors, gardening, enjoys traveling and spending time with her husband, daughter, friends and family.

Learn more about Kim, her articles, her travels and updated veteran information, go to www.MilitaryResourceBooks.com.

Follow Kim on Twitter: @OpMilResources

Follow Kim on Facebook: OperationMilitaryResources

ACKNOWLEDGMENTS

Putting a book together takes a lot of thought, planning and a vision that at times can be hard to express, even with words. I am lucky to have an awesome editor and book designer; Alane Pearce who agreed to work with me again even knowing how frustrating this project was going to be. Alane's work is impeccable; she saw my vision, need for time, and did an exceptional job. Learn more about Alane at www.MyPublishingCoach.com.

This year I was ecstatic to welcome Maria Connor to my team; she is a creative, visionary web designer (and an author as well) and really works hard to keep my website updated, creative and informative-despite all of my crazy calls and demands; it was a stroke of luck to find another amazing woman who understood my vision and my jokes, and laughs at my electronic illiteracy. . Maria was instrumental in connecting me with social media via Facebook and Twitter. Both of these ladies are Rock Stars and I am honored to be working with them. Thank you for honoring me and working together to get this book published and promoted to assist our military community. Learn more about Maria at www.myauthorconcierge.com.

I need to thank Pam, Doreatha and Pat for their assistance with coming over, computers in hand to help verify all these resources before I listed them...This was very helpful!! Thank you to my friends and family for understanding the missed events and lack of phone calls.

Thank you to the VFW Headquarters for the State of Michigan, Our Military Kids, Battling Bare, several friends and community donations for the pictures in this book. Your support and trust in the usage of these photos means a lot to me

To my husband, Steve and daughter Cheyenne, thank you for your support and understanding when I missed events, didn't cook, had a grouchy attitude and a paper mess all over the house. I love you and appreciate your love and support.

DISCLAIMER

Some of the information contained in this book has come directly from the organization's brochure or website; I did this so I didn't misrepresent an organization by inferring or interpreting their organization's mission.

No endorsements by The Department of Defense or the US Armed Forces are implied to Kimberly Suchek, this book nor the organizations listed herein.

Care has been taken to ensure that the information in this book was accurate at the time of publication, July 2015. Be advised that addresses, phone numbers, emails, etc..., may change and that companies may go out of business or change their products and services. Kimberly is happy to receive corrections, comments and suggestions for future editions.

The author of this book, and anyone associated with the publication of this book, is not responsible for a link that doesn't work, an organization that no longer exists, or any other issues associated with the reader's experience, mishaps, alleged to be caused, directly or indirectly by information contained in this book.

This book is meant to be a source of help for military families, but not a definitive list or an official endorsement of any para-military organization listed herein. We did our best to make sure all the links in this document work; if a link doesn't work, we are sorry. With almost 300 pages of them, we were bound to miss a few! Just let us know and we'll fix it in the next edition and online at www.MilitaryResourceBooks.com.

If you know of a resource not listed in this edition or in VOL 1, please contact the author at http://militaryresourcebooks.com and suggest it for promotion on website and future editions of Operation Military Resources.

Find out more about Kimberly Suchek, further military news, updates and events at http://MilitaryResourceBooks.com.

Follow Kimberly on Facebook and Twitter:
http://www.facebook.com/OperationMilitaryResources
http://www.twitter.com/@OpMilResources.

Table of Contents

BASIC INFORMATION
YOU SHOULD KNOW

When creating this edition of Operation Military Resources, I tossed around several thoughts on what to do with this book and this chapter in particular. I had to ask myself, do I want to update what I have created or share more resources. At first, my thought was about money being spent on another book with the same information already shared in the first. So was an update more important than sharing further resources?

Ultimately my decision to write and share all new resources, with an addition of some favorites and updates on other benefits and resources won the debate. My reasoning is simple; many military families and/ or organizations who do not own my first copy need to be aware of "The Basic Things You Should Know" as it is an intricate part of our lives. In many cases if the little things are in place it stops many of the bigger issues from even beginning. And of course, listing new resources in my mind is providing you with further options when needed.

Remember, the military community is tight and the family structure is not typical or the norm. Instead, our family structure consists (in most cases) one parent gone most of the year on a deployment or in training. The norm is one parent home, holding down the fort and making sure everything is done all while trying to regularly update the missing spouse to promote a feeling of inclusion for the military member. These updates are usually accomplished by Skype, email, phone calls, letters or other creative means of communication. Each spouse in a military marriage deals with issues that the average married couple would never encounter, never find important and in some cases would never understand. It takes a unique person to be able to live the military life and be successful at it. I hope this book can assist you in your journey.

With a few basic tools in place (and a basic understanding of) will make life for a military family easier. Briefly I will be highlighting them for your review.

Defense Enrollment Eligibility Reporting System (DEERS)

DEERS is simply a database of those who are eligible for **TRICARE** and other military benefits. In the military, unless you and your family are registered in **DEERS** you do not exist. Service members get automatically enrolled when they enter the military, but even their status and rank/status changes need to be updated. After you are registered in **DEERS**, you can take advantage of the same benefits your service member enjoys, such as a military ID card which allows you on bases, **TRICARE health care**, shopping at the **Base Exchange and Commissary**, discounts at stores and flights on space A travel (discussed later).

To enroll, go with your service member to a **DEERS** site on base and your service member will fill out a DD Form 1172 (an application for **Department of Defense Common Access Card and DEERS Enrollment**) for each eligible family member and be prepared to provide identification, which needs to include one picture ID (drivers license, passport, state ID card) and supporting documentation such as a marriage and birth certificate and Social Security cards. Don't forget to update **DEERS** as needed. For example, you'll need to notify **DEERS** for death certificates, newborns, service member's retirement information, etc. The service member must be with you when you enroll in **DEERS** and get your ID card unless he is deployed under Title 10 Orders. If this is the case, bring a copy of your spouse's orders, power of attorney paperwork (some sites want to see this documentation) along with other supporting documentation. If you are not available to be at a **DEERS** site with your service member when he is updating, he/she may print out an extra copy of the 1172 Form and bring it to you to go an obtain your military ID card (and dependents) without your sponsor present. This form will allow you 30 days from time it was printed.

Any time you or your service member experience a significant life event, update **DEERS** within 30 days. If you don't, you may experience a break in your benefits.

If you need assistance locating an ID office, visit the Rapids Site Locator at: http://www.dmdc.osd.mil/rsl/appj/ site?execution=e1s1. You can search for the nearest office by Zip code, city or state. After you have that information, make sure you call the office to verify its location and business hours first. Most sites only issue ID cards certain days of the week and/or at certain times of the day.

If you are the spouse of a service member, dependent child over the age of 10 or the child from divorced or single parents, no matter the age, you need to get an ID card. Remember, military ID cards have to be renewed every four years or when a service member has a change of status from non-active duty to active duty. Military ID cards are also your health insurance cards www.dmdc.osd.mil.

Health Care (TRICARE)

One of the most significant financial benefits service members and their families receive from the military is free health care when they are on Title 32 and 10 orders and discount health care cost when they are state employees (technicians) for the military working in the armories. One of the hardest cost of any individual is medical coverage, especially dental and vision plus dealing with cost associated with prescriptions.

Most civilian retirees do not have employer- provided health care and if they do the costs, such as premiums and copays randomly go up or items drop off the covered list. Sometimes coverage is not even guaranteed to last through their retirement. (This happened to my father after 20 years at Motor Wheel and retirement he lost all medical. This is not fair nor should it be legal)

And they almost never have vision or dental coverage. However, those employed in, or retired from, the armed forces—and their families—have access to very affordable, quality health care and insurance guaranteed for life by the U.S. government. (Well, with laws and the government on the path they are things are dropping off the covered list...but we can hope for better support).

Here is a brief rundown of health care plan choices. This includes, spouse, widow/widower (if not remarried), unmarried children under age 26 and dependent parents and in-laws. Also, former spouses qualify if they are not remarried and they are not eligible for private medical insurance. I will not go into major detail about the different options but this is something you will need to review in more detail; please review the TRICARE website for specifics http://www. tricare.mil.

TRICARE "Standard" Provides you with the greatest flexibility to choose health care providers, without a referral or pre-authorization, but it also costs the most. It is available worldwide

TRICARE "Extra" is more restrictive and less expensive. You pay the same annual deductible as those with Standard; however your share of medical costs is 5% less. This plan is only available in the continental United States (CONUS).

TRICARE "Prime" is like an HMO and is geared toward preventive care. It is the least expensive option, but your choice of health care providers is limited. You pay very little and in some cases, nothing at all.

All active-duty service members and activated Guard and Reserve are required to enroll themselves and their family into TRICARE Prime or one of the Prime options, depending on where they live and work. All other eligible beneficiaries may choose to enroll in TRICARE Prime. If eligible beneficiaries don't enroll in TRICARE Prime, they are automatically covered by TRICARE Standard and Extra.

A few things you need to keep in mind when using TRICARE. There is a difference between "authorized" health care providers that are part of a network and "authorized" providers that are non-network providers, and also between participating providers and non-participating providers.

Authorized Health Care Providers may be part of a network of contracted providers who accept TRICARE negotiated payments and file claims for you.

Other Authorized Health Care Providers are non-network providers, they have no contract with TRICARE and they limit their services to a case-by-case-basis. You may or may not be able to access TRICARE paid services from authorized non-network providers. You will want to ask if they are familiar with TRICARE before you use their services if they are new to you.

Participating providers accept TRICARE benefits as payment in full, file claims for you and won't bill you for additional costs for their services.

Non-Participating providers may charge you up to 15% more than the TRICARE allowable charge. You may be responsible for paying for treatment at the time of service and filing your own claims with TRICARE for reimbursement.

TRICARE will only pay for care provided by authorized providers. Medicare certified hospitals must participate in TRICARE for inpatient care. However, for outpatient care, providers have the choice whether or not to become authorized providers.

Just ask your doctors before you use their services. If they are not authorized, explain that you do not wish to go to another doctor. Most do not want to lose business and it is easy enough for them to call TRICARE and fill out a form to keep your business. To find out if your provider is TRICARE authorized, check with your regional TRICARE service center at http://tricare.mil/contactus.

Also, if you are a state military worker and you have health insurance that you pay for, while you are on active duty orders, your premium is paid for by the federal government. This is very helpful if you have dependents. While you are deployed they use whatever health care you had as primary and then use TRICARE as secondary insurance. This will take care of most health care bills and prescription costs while deployed. Check with your local HMO office for more details.

The Catastrophic Cap for active duty and National Guard is $1,000. Retirees, family members of retirees, survivors, and former spouse are $3,000 per fiscal year.

Additional TRICARE Services

TRICARE Prime Remote: If you live more than 50 miles away from a military treatment facility your family can still participate in a program very similar to TRICARE Prime—it's called TRICARE Prime Remote. Instead of obtaining treatment at your local military treatment facility, you see a local civilian health care provider who is part of the TRICARE authorized network. Activated Guard and Reserve members and their families are eligible also. For more information about TRICARE prime remote visit http://mybenefit/home/overview/plans/primeremote.

If using TRICARE Prime Remote and having requested medical assistance, go to www.mytricare.com and you can verify if your bill has been approved through your TRICARE program. If you go to the doctor before it is approved, you can pay for it and get reimbursed at a later date.

Please Note: There is a difference between TRICARE Prime and TRICARE Prime Remote. When a Guard or Reserve member gets activated, they have a choice; TRICARE Standard or TRICARE Prime Remote (NOT Prime). After deployment military families fall into **TAMP**, which will be Standard TRICARE. If they wish to have TRICARE Prime or TRICARE Prime Remote they will need to re-enroll.

TRICARE Prime Overseas: This works the same as TRICARE Prime in areas where there are military facilities and a network of civilian providers. The difference is if a provider is not available in your location, you may have your share of point-of-service costs waived by getting your primary care manager to refer you to a regional medical service center, which is a TRICARE authorized health care provider. But the point of service option is NOT available to active-duty military or activated Guard or Reserve members. For assistance with TRICARE Prime Overseas, call 888-777-8343 or visit http://mybenefit/home/ overview/plans/primeoverseas.

TRICARE Reserve Select: Available worldwide to most selected Reserve members and their families while not on active duty. You have the freedom to manage your own health care and utilize any TRICARE authorized provider. You may also access care at a military treatment facility. With TRICARE Reserve Select you get health care coverage for service members and dependents for a small premium each month and annual deductibles unless treatment is at a military treatment facility then no deductible applies. In my last book I stated the monthly premium and co-pays but as cost associated with medical is rapidly changing I do not wish to miss-inform you or your families.

Cost range is dependent on rank. Your share of most medical services, device and supplies costs including outpatient, clinical preventive, laboratory and X-ray, maternity, ambulance and emergency services should be as high as 15% of allowable charges if approved and provided by a network provider. If services are rendered by a non-network provider, your share of allowable charges could be as high as 20%. Your cost for hospitalization, newborn care or inpatient skilled nursing treatment is at least $15 per day, subject to at least a $25 minimum (remember these costs are subject to DoD budgets yearly and subject to change). In most cases there is minimal or no cost to access treatment at a military treatment facility. Generally you have to pay for services when they are rendered and seek reimbursement by submitting a claim form to TRICARE Reserve Select. TRICARE Reserve Select is an excellent option if you and your family are eligible. This program provides comprehensive health care at a reasonable cost and includes the TRICARE prescription drug coverage.

Updates to the TRICARE program that started in 2011 are as follows:

TRICARE Young Adult (TYA): A new premium-based health care plan for adult dependent children up to age 26. It can be purchased after eligibility coverage ends at age 21, or 23 if enrolled in a full course of study at an approved institution of higher learning. TYA provides access to medical and pharmacy benefits, but does not include dental.

TYA-TRICARE Standard is available worldwide, but TRICARE Prime will not be available until a later date. TYA participants may visit any TRICARE –authorized provider, network or non-network provider but care at a military treatment facility is on a case by case basis only. TYA do not need a referral for any type of care but some services may require prior authorization. The type of provider determines how much the amount of out-of-pocket expenses will cost. Just remember visiting a network provider will result in less out of pocket, in addition to the convenience of having the network provider file the claims directly.

Requirements to Remember:

TYA must be a dependent of an eligible uniformed service sponsor. If the sponsor is a non-activated member of the Selected Reserve of the Ready Reserve or of the Retired Reserve, the sponsor must be enrolled in the TRICARE Reserve Select or TRICARE Retired Reserve for the dependent to be eligible to purchase TRICARE Young Adult coverage.

TYA must be unmarried, at least 21 but not yet 26 years old (NOTE: those enrolled in a full course of study at an approved institution of higher learning and their sponsor provided 50% of their financial support, their eligibility may not begin until age 23).

Dependent is not eligible to enroll in an employer-sponsored health plan based on his or her own employment and not otherwise eligible for other TRICARE coverage.

TYA is pay-to-play program requiring eligible dependents to apply a monthly premium. TYA premium rates are established annually on a calendar year bases. The 2011 monthly premium was $181+ per month.

Vision Benefits

TRICARE Prime participants must be age three (3) and older (there are special rules for newborns and infants or if you or a family member has diabetes) and are entitled to vision benefits, including comprehensive eye exams once every two (2) years. You don't even have to work through your primary care manager for a referral or authorization unless you can't or don't want to see a network provider. TRICARE covers some surgeries and treatments for diseases and conditions of the eyes. You can even get free eyeglasses from your local military treatment facility.

Vision exams are only provided to military members and families who have TRICARE Prime coverage. Those families covered by TRICARE Standard or Extra are not eligible unless the exam is necessary due to a covered medical condition. For additional information about all military health programs, visit the TRICARE website at http://www.tricare.osd.mil.

Dental Benefits

The **TRICARE Dental Plan (TDP)** is available to the military families of active-duty or activated Guard or Reserve. Active duty and activated Guard and Reserve receive free dental care from the military dental treatment facilities. If a facility is not close to you then you can have your treatment approved by TRICARE prior to treatment from your dental office.

Dental Insurance is premium-base insurance; TRICARE monitors it, but it is contracted through United Concordia Companies, Inc. The TRICARE Dental Program (TDP) is portable and is covered worldwide, so when your sponsor changes duty stations, you don't have to change dental plans. Coverage and costs on TDP changes for National Guard and Reserve members and their families as the sponsor's status changes from inactive to active duty. Your cost will be less, so remember to keep your DEERS information up-to-date. You are eligible for TDP if you are family members of active duty uniformed service personal, family members of the National Guard and Reserve Service Member who are active duty and not active. Family members include spouses, unmarried children (including step-children, adopted children and court-appointed wards) under the age of 21. Unmarried children are eligible up to the end of the month in which they turn 21 and may be eligible up to age 23 in certain circumstances. Sponsor must have 12 months remaining on obligation of the military (this is waived if deployed or being deployed).

Those not eligible for Dental Insurance are: Active duty service members including National Guard and Reserve members called or ordered to active duty for more than 30 days; retired service members and their families; former spouses, parents and parents in law, disabled veterans, and foreign military personnel.

I will not go into all costs and amounts related to TDP, please review the details online at www.tricaredentalprogram.com or call 800-866-8499 if you are in United States and 888-418-0466 OCONUS.

There are a few things I would like you to keep in mind when you are deciding on dental coverage:

For eligible family members, the monthly premiums for TDP are a set price for a single family and with two or more. Since premium can change I will not state the premium. First monthly premium is due upon enrollment, if your spouse is on active duty you can have premium deducted from his/her paycheck. If spouse is not activated, service members' premium will be taken from paycheck and families will be billed separately. Keep in mind premiums are cheaper when service member is activated, so make sure you update when necessary.

The maximum annual benefit any one beneficiary can receive is $1,200 and lifetime maximum orthodontic benefit is $1,500 per beneficiary. Remember these amounts are subject to change per DoD, check costs before making any decisions or commitments.

Once enrolled in TDP, you must continue the coverage and pay premiums for at least 12 months. After the first 12 months your enrollment commitment is only month-to-month. Also, if you enroll after 21st of the month, coverage does not start until the beginning of the following two months. For example, if you enroll June 14, coverage starts July 1st. If you don't enroll until June 21, coverage will not start until Aug. 1st .

The TRICARE dental plan covers all of the costs for diagnostic, emergency and preventive services. This is all based on your service member's status and rank. If you need assistance enrolling in the TRICARE Dental Plan contact United Concordia at 888-622-2256 or www.ucci.com.

Prescription Drug Coverage

If you are using TRICARE health care benefits, you are eligible for the TRICARE Prescription Drug Plan. The coverage is the same for all military health care plans and is available worldwide. There are four (4) different ways to have your prescriptions filled:

Military Pharmacies: The military treatment facility pharmacy is your best option if your prescription is available there. You can get a 90-day supply at no cost. It's a good idea to call ahead to verify that your prescription is available.

Mail Order Pharmacies: This is a great alternative if your prescription drug isn't available through the MTF. You can save money, but you must plan in advance. Depending on the pharmacy, the mail service and your location, it could take several days to receive your prescription. As of OCT 2011, there is no copayments for generic prescription medications for 90- day supplies through TRICARE Home Delivery while the copayments for the same medication increased in costs. For more information visit the TRICARE mail order pharmacy program online at http://www.express-scripts.com/tricare

Network Pharmacies: If your prescription needs to be filled immediately and it is not carried by your local MTF, you will need to obtain it through a network pharmacy. To find a network pharmacies go to http://express-scriptspharmacy.com/TRICARE/

Non-Network Pharmacies: The more expensive option is non-network pharmacies. These pharmacies do not partner with TRICARE and you will have to pay full price for your prescriptions.

If you have access to the Internet, the easiest way to enroll in any TRICARE program is online at http://www.tricare. mil/ mybenefit/home/medical. You will need certain information to complete your enrollment application whether you are enrolling online, mailing your application or faxing it. Go to the website and follow steps to set up your profile. Once your application has been processed you will receive a package by mail, including a welcome letter identifying your primary care manager, if one has been assigned to you, and enrollment card for each family member who is enrolled, and a copy of the TRICARE Handbook.

There have been many changes to TRICARE Remote and costs associated with location and availability for active and retirees. Rank structure still dictates the costs and co-pays; go to the website and make sure you and your families still qualify before signing up to stop any difficulties with medical coverage.

Other Support Within The Military

There are times when we all feel like we are not getting the support needed or required. For various reasons we do not wish to speak with friends, family or even our spouse. Please remember there are other resources for you, and you don't have to live near an installation to use them.

Chapel: Some bases offer services and ceremonies at the chapel on base, but those that do not still have a chaplain and they offer support to service members and families before, during and after deployments. Remember, most chaplains have deployed and faced the same issues that you and your family are going through. Chaplains have many resources and are confidential.

Family Support Centers: Family Support Centers can be a wealth of resources and provide loads of information about military life including deployments, before and after, financial management, job search, moves, volunteer opportunities, marital, family and individual (confidential) counseling, and more.

Clubs and Groups: There are various clubs and groups within a base and off base in which you can participate. These can consist of Family Readiness Groups, church groups and spouse clubs. There are also organizations such as, the Veterans of Foreign Wars (VFW), American Legion and Operation Homefront, just to name a few. These are terrific resources that can help you feel a great sense of belonging while befriending and communicating with people who understand what you are going through.

Family Advocacy Programs (FAP): Sometimes in our lives, things happen that are out of our control. If that happens, or if you or anyone you know is a victim of abuse or even just major stress, the counselors and experts at Family Advocacy can help. FAP is your resource for child and spouse abuse prevention as well as preventive education classes, such as crisis management, parenting and anger management. They even have support groups for new parents and parents of deployed single soldiers.

Military Acronyms: Helpful site for you to learn the abbreviations and Acronyms that are widely used in the military world.
http://www.dtic.mil/doctrine/dod_dictionary/index.html

Glossary Information: This site features a glossary of terms relating to military quality of life programs as well as other links to additional glossaries that you may find helpful.
http://glossarist.com/glossaries/government-politicsmilitary/military/default.asp

Military Pay

I remember saying in my last book how surprised I would get when assisting a spouse of a service member with financial assistance and find they had NO CLUE as to how much their service member earned. Or the fact they did not know how to read a LES or even what it was.

Sometimes they were miss-informed, did not pay attention or my favorite "told to wait for their pay check from the military," Now, I just find this situation (depending on my mood) funny, sad or frustrating. To me the idea of a spouse being clueless regarding such concepts as special pay, allowances, a yearly raise, and flight pay etc....is very frustrating. A spouse should not be in a situation of financial emergency and not be able to fill out the form because of lack of knowledge or miss-information; this makes her, the family and the military look bad in the eyes of the organization wishing to assist. Please keep this in mind.

My last book frustrated many of you for letting the "cat out of the bag" so to speak, but don't military families go through enough? Why should a spouse have to sacrifice more than they already do, or scramble to find money to fix something when the service member has the money and the spouse does not know? Again, please keep this in mind; if you fear a spouse spending all your money while deployed there are steps you can take in regards to Power of Attorney etc.... please put these in place.

Things to remember regarding pay:

Basic pay, allowances and special pay are affected by the service member's military occupation, pay grade, where they are stationed and deployment status. I will attempt to give you just a brief description of these so that you can see what may apply to your family and goals.

Basic Pay: This is your service member's base paycheck and they are the same across all branches of the service. The only differences in basic pay are pay grade and, to a small degree, the number of years your service member has been in the service.

Additional Pay: Your service member may qualify for additional pay because of any unique training or specialty, where his/her duty station is located and whether they are in a combat zone. Your family may also receive allowances for food, clothing and shelter.

The following is a list of specialty pay and bonuses:

- **Hazardous Duty Pay**: While your service member is deployed overseas on Title 10 Orders, he/she is usually getting paid more money. The activities and situations they are exposed to dictate the compensation. (The cost amount may be different depending on budgets and the year, this is based on 2012)

- **$225 per month for Hostile Fire and Imminent Danger Pay:** Additional pay for those occasions when your service member is subject to hostile fire or explosion.

- **$50 to $150 per month for Hardship Duty Pay:** For service member living and working in extremely difficult living conditions or enduring excessive physical hardship.

- **$150 per month for Hazardous Duty Incentive Pay:** In addition to living and working in a danger zone, under extremely difficult living conditions, your service member may also perform particularly hazardous duties such as jumping out of airplanes or handling explosives.

- **$150 to $350 per month for Hazardous Duty Incentive Pay for Flying**: Service member or aircrews (except pilots) receive this additional pay. Pilots are paid additionally for their job specialty but it is in a different category.

Your service member is only entitled to any two of these hazardous duty pays that apply at any one time.

There has been many changes to TRICARE Remote and costs associated with location and availability for active and retirees. Rank structure still dictates the costs and co-pays; go to the website and make sure you and your families still qualify before signing up to stop any difficulties with medical coverage.

Unique Training or Specialty Pay: Each branch of the armed services pays extra if the service member acquires the unique skills or specialized training for certain military occupations; he/she may also be eligible for certain bonuses. For example, aviation officers earn an extra $125 to $840 per month. Sea duty brings $50-$730 a month, and diving duty up to $340 per month. Proficiency in a foreign language that has been deemed critical can earn up to $1000 per month in extra income.

• **Special Bonuses**: The military offers certain bonus to help encourage service members to continue longer retention of its service members. This can be important for not only specialty fields but also for the extra cost it would be to retrain service members.

• **Re-enlistment**: Bonuses vary depending on training, specialty, willingness to accept undesirable assignments and length of service. It is sad to think after so many years they no longer get bonuses to re-enlist but that is the way the government works.

• **Pilot**: Up to $25,000 per year for aviators remaining on active duty after the end of their initial enlistment.

• **Nuclear**: Up to $20,000 one-time bonus is available to naval officers upon their selection for nuclear power training duty. An additional annual pay of up to $22,000 is provided for their technical qualifications for duty in nuclear propulsion plants. And if they sign a long-term contract, they may be entitled to an additional $25,000 bonus each year.

• **JAG**: Up to $60,000 is available to officers who complete ten years of service as a judge advocate.

• **Medical**: Special pay is awarded to medical officers if they agree to remain on active duty for at least one year after their service obligation. Remaining on active duty after their initial service obligation period provides up to $14,000 per year of additional pay.

• **Dental**: Up to $30,000 is available to officers who contract to serve on active duty for over four years. An additional $7,000 to $27,000 per year is paid for their unique skills, and even more if they are board certified.

• **Veterinary**: Veterinary officers are eligible to receive awards of $2,000 to $5,000 per year depending on their years of service. In addition they receive an extra $100 per month in special pay.

• **Special Warfare**: Officers who remain on active duty in special warfare service for at least one year may be entitled to receive a continuation bonus of up to $15,000 per year, for each year they serve on special warfare duty.

Allowances

In addition to their basic paycheck with any additional special pay they may earn, your military member receives a family allowance if he is married or has other dependents. These allowances are to help cover increases in the cost of living, as well as additional expenses related to food, clothing and shelter if they live off base.

Cost of Living Allowance (COLA): The cost of living varies from city to city. Since basic pay is the same no matter where you live, the military will provide a monthly cost of living allowance (COLA) to help make up this imbalance in compensation.

COLA depends on the assigned duty station, pay grade, length of time in the service and whether there are dependents. If you live in a location that the military regards as a high cost area, you will receive a COLA increase whether you live on base or off. Visit www.military.com/cola to calculate the current COLA adjustment for various locations and your personal situation.

Basic Allowance for Subsistence (BAS): This shows as BAS on your pay stub and is intended to offset the cost of food for the military member NOT THE FAMILY. The amount is adjusted annually. The monthly BAS paid to an officer is about $200 and the amount provided to enlisted is almost $300. This allowance is paid to all military members whether they dine in the mess hall or off base. Be careful with this though, as government-provided meals are only partially subsidized.

Clothing Allowances: Service members receive a one-time payment clothing allowance after commissioning to buy clothing. Enlisted receive uniforms and an annual clothing maintenance allowance. If your service member is required to wear civilian duds as part of his duty assignment, the service will provide an allowance for this additional expense.

Per Diem: While traveling on official military business, the military member is entitled to a daily allotment to reimburse them for the cost of food and lodging so the military member does not have to use money out of their pockets to pay for the business trip. To check the per diem rate for your state, go to http://perdiem.hqda.pentagon.mil/perdiem.

Housing Allowances (BAH): Basic Allowance for Housing (also known as BAH) is provided to service members to adjust for the additional costs of living off base. The actual amount of BAH is based on the local rental housing market, pay grade and number of dependents. Keep a couple of things in mind when you are adding up the housing allowance; first, BAH is a set amount and your actual housing expense can be higher than your BAH. You can review this at http://www.defensetravel.dod.mil/site/bah.cfm

Second, BAH is paid out automatically when you apply for off base housing and if you and your spouse are both employed by the military, each of you is entitled to the BAH. If you live together, one of you can claim BAH with dependents and the other must register at the single rate. You should have the service member with the highest pay grade claim dependents so you receive the highest BAH. If a service member is stationed overseas and lives off base, they don't receive BAH. Instead they receive Special Overseas Housing Allowance, or OHA. This allowance is intended to offset the actual coast of rent, utilities and recurring maintenance expenses. Unlike BAH, OHA is NOT a set monthly amount. While you are eligible for OHA, you also qualify for a move-in housing allowance to cover the purchase of necessities; one-time fees, such as real estate agent fees or lease taxes; and reimbursements for required security expenses. If you are unable to stay in government housing when you first report to a permanent duty station outside of the USA (OCONUS) for some other reason beyond your control, you may be eligible for an overseas temporary lodging allowance; generally up to 60 days.

Dislocation Allowance: A military member or family must periodically relocate due to a change in duty stations or as required by the government. A dislocation allowance or DLA ranging from about $1,800 to nearly $4,000 is granted to help offset your relocation expenses. The DLA rate is dependent on pay grade. This allowance does not apply toward the costs your family incurs locating to the first duty station after initial training.

Family Separation Allowance (FSA): When your service member is away for more than 30 days, you are entitled to the Family Separation Allowance of $250 per month. If your service member is assigned to a permanent duty station where dependents are not allowed or if your spouse is on duty on board a ship at sea for more than 30 days you will be entitled to the FSA.

Time Off and Leave

Military members earn two and a half days leave per month, or 30 days each year. Service members leave can accumulate for up to 75 days--over two full years and if they don't use it they will lose it.

Active duty unable to take leave because of operational duties may carry forward as many as 120 days leave for up to three to four years depending on circumstances. This carryover happens automatically. If the active duty member retires or transitions out of the armed forces with unused leave, they may receive a cash buyout of their unused leave. Enlisted service members may now sell back up to 30 days of special accrued leave earned in a combat zone or designated contingency operation. This is an especially valuable benefit because payment for leave earned under these circumstances is not taxed, however you can't cash out more than sixty (60) days' worth of leave.

Military Provided Life Insurance

I am glad our newly enlisted military take this benefit to heart and make sure everything is in place when they first join. I need them to take this one-step further and update this immediately when changes occur. In a society where the divorce rate is high you need to make sure this type of documentation is updated as well. It does not matter if DEERS states you divorced and have a new spouse. If you did not change the name of the beneficiary ALL your life insurance will go to the ex-spouse. Or if you are married and policy was left to parents. Please remember and stay current on all paperwork. This is a situation I have come across time and time again. And in several of these situations the parents (or whoever was listed as beneficiary) did not give any assistance to the spouse, because they hated her/him.

This needs to be taken seriously: MAKE SURE LIFE INSURANCE POLICIES ARE UPDATED!!

Active Duty personnel are offered through DoD a $400,000 Life insurance policy which is offered at time of enlistment with policy payments allotted out of paychecks at $29 per month. Again, I will briefly touch on the subject. Contact your local unit or Family Assistance Center for more information.

Service Members Group Life Insurance (SGLI) is available to all active duty and members of the National Guard and Reserves. Active Duty personnel are offered through DoD a $400,000 life insurance policy which is offered at time of enlistment with policy payments allotted out of paychecks at $29 per month. If a service member wishes to reduce, change or cancel coverage they need to fill out the SGLI Election and Certificate Form 3286 and turn in to their HMO office.

This coverage stays in effect for the duration of the military career and converts into Veterans Group Life Insurance (VGLI) with no medical underwriting upon transitioning from the military. Just remember conversion from SGLI to VGLI MUST take place within 120 days of retirement to avoid medical underwriting.

If you wish to have more life insurance coverage, here is a list of companies that are military friendly (basically because they don't have a war clause).

Check out the following websites for additional information.

www.usaa.com (my favorite)

www.usba.com

www.moaa.org

www.navymutual.org (Navy and Marines)

www.aafmaa.com (Army and Air Force)

www.afba.com

Along with the $29 monthly payment for SGLI at $400,000, a $1 per month premium is automatically included for Traumatic Injury Protection coverage (TIPC). This is a mandatory coverage and provides benefit between $25,000 and $100,000 if your soldier sustains one of the following Traumatic Injuries: Loss of sight, speech or hearing , loss of one hand or foot, or a major injury to the hand, severe paralysis, burns or brain injury. The military also provides a Families Service Member Group Life Insurance Policy (FSGLI). This policy covers $250,000 for your spouse and $10,000 for each of your dependent children. The cost for your spouse under 35 is $5.50 a month (deducted from your paycheck) and no cost coverage for dependent children. This premium increases at a very affordable amount every five years. For more information on FSGLI visit www.insurance.va.gov/sglisite/fsgli/ sglifam.Htm

Legal Rights/Legal Issues

As a military family you have many legal rights and protections. Laws have been passed to secure these rights; unfortunately some people will try to abuse military families. Make sure you are aware of your rights and do not be afraid to use them. One of the biggest rights you have is called **The Service Members Civil Relief Act (SCRA) also known as Soldiers & Sailors Relief Act.** This law helps insure your family's legal rights. The law covers all active duty service members, activated Guard and Reserve, and their dependent family members. These laws were put in place to allow your service member to focus on the job and minimize undue financial hardship on the military family. To further minimize hardship on your family, the Armed Services provide legal assistance to all active-duty, Guard and Reserve members, and their dependent family members. I will list some of the highlights of the SCRA that you should familiarize yourself with:

•**Limit on Interest Rates:** Interest rates that the service member must pay on any loan or debt that they had prior to active duty are limited to no more than 6% a year. However, this cap on your interest rates is NOT automatic. You must contact your lender in writing and request this benefit change. They will require a copy of your service member's orders and sometimes a copy of the Power of Attorney. Remember these are debts that include both spouse's names and/or military member's name alone but NOT debts that list only spouse name. Some companies like SEARS and Military Star card, will even go farther and put your account on a deployment hold. This means you are NOT required to make payments on the account while your military member is deployed. This will not affect your credit rating negatively. These companies deserve praise for making this extra gesture. For some families this really helps!! Speak to your creditors and you will be surprised at how many will go the extra mile.

• **Stay of Proceedings**: If you are involved in a lawsuit you can request a delay, if the delay is necessary due to your service member's service. For example, if the service member cannot show up for court. This DOES include child support cases and custody cases.

• **Statute of Limitations**: Your active-duty service member's service to our country will not be taken into account when determining the statute of limitations on legal proceedings brought by or against you.

• **Health Insurance Reinstatement:** If the service member has health insurance prior to reporting to active duty, SCRA requires your civilian health insurance company to reinstate coverage when the service member completes their service.

• **Home Foreclosure Protection:** Your mortgage company can't foreclose on you if you have a mortgage prior to active duty and you can prove that military service is the reason you can't afford to make your mortgage payment. Remember, mortgages fall under the 6% cap also.

• **Eviction Protection:** Your landlord also has to be more flexible if you are renting your home and can't keep up with your rent payments because of your service member's duty. They are also required by law to let you out of any contract if you get activated or PCS'd (moved) without any backlash of court or marks to your credit report.

• **Business Lease Termination:** Your service member can terminate a business lease (even one that has both your names on it) contract that you or your spouse had prior to active duty if reporting to duty would make continuing that lease unreasonable. That does not include walking away from back payments or abandoning the building the minute orders are issued. You will be responsible for all past payments through (most cases) the end of the next month. You must give the lease holder/landlord written notice along with a copy of your order and in some cases power of attorney paperwork if the spouse is cancelling on behalf of the service member. Remember this includes leasing cars and in some cases recently purchased cars.

• **Eliminates Double Taxation:** If you or your service member work in one state, but your legal residence is in a different state, SCRA prevents the state in which you're employed from taxing your income. Only your state of residence may tax your income. (Hopefully your legal residence is one of the few states without state income tax). Remember the new ruling is that spouses no longer have to change

In addition to the protections provided by SCRA, Guard and Reserve families and service members receive additional protections under the **Uniformed Services Employment and Reemployment Rights Act (USERRA).** The biggest provision under USERRA is the law that requires employers to reemploy Guard and Reserve members when they return from deployment. The exception would be if the company went out of business. Not only is the employer required to re-employ service members returning to the civilian work force, but employers must also re-employ the reservist in a position comparable to the one they had prior to going on active duty along with full seniority, pay and any further benefits they had.

Most states have **Legal Assistance Centers (JAG)** for military families that assist if you are having trouble with any legal issues or any of your rights under the laws. In addition to answering questions about your legal rights and protections, your legal assistance center can assist you by drafting a will and creating health care directives and powers of attorney. Legal assistance attorneys can also answer questions and give advice about your income taxes or any other personal legal issues. Remember this is at NO COST to you. To find a legal assistance center near you visit http://legalassistance. law.af.mil/ content/locator.php. Also your JAG office can assist with some legal issues and may have this contact information at hand.

Don't forget your Family Support Center! They are loaded with resources and contact information about benefits for military families. Most centers are staffed with people who've been through transitions, deployments and reunions. They have spouses in the service and kids in the local schools. The staff can help you locate discount day care **(NACCRA)** get you information about programs for the kids and summer camps. They will also have information about grants and scholarships.

Power of Attorney

I have spoken of this document briefly above so I want to state again how important it is to have one in place, not only during deployments but also in day-to-day life. This document enables you to appoint someone to make financial decisions and manage your financial affairs in the event that you can't do this for yourself. Most couples appoint each other as their financial power of attorney. But, you should also select a successor, so that in the event your spouse is unable or unavailable to perform these services, you've got a backup. Your military legal assistance office can also assist you in obtaining these documents.

You should also consider a Living Trust and/or Living Will and Durable Power of Attorney for health care. I should also mention "Accounting for ownership and beneficiary designation" which means all assets that transfer by title or beneficiary designation upon death avoid probate. You can reduce probate expenses and hassles by maximizing your use of appropriate ownership classifications. There are many specifics regarding this so I advise counsel with your legal advisor.

Questions/Concerns:

If you have a question, comment or need assistance and cannot find the resource information in this book or in my first edition; feel free to contact me at Kim@MilitaryResourceBooks.com. Make sure you sign up for updates on my website at www.MilitaryResourceBooks.com, and follow me on Facebook and Twitter for great information, resources and updated (civilian/military) news at http://www.facebook.com/OperationMilitaryResources, and http://www.twitter.com/@OpMilResources

To purchase a copy of the first edition of Operation Military Resources go to www.MilitaryResourceBooks.com.

If you are interested in bulk orders for your group or constituents, please contact Kimberly for an estimated discount. Let's work together to help our military families!

SERVICE MEMBER

Current, Veterans, Retirees, Wounded and Homeless

In my last book I listed all these titles separate and it seemed to cause some confusion and repetition of resources. It's important to remember any person man/woman who has served is a veteran. The only difference lies in the years you were in, your deployments and the type of transition you made. I have listed Wounded and Homeless in a sub-title as there are specific resources only for those veterans. Plus as in the last book I listed employment, education, legal, financial assistance and retreats for the service member in a sub-title as well. Various other resources I have left in alphabetical order for your review.

Absentee Voting: The Federal Voting Assistance Program is a program in the DoD that helps ensure military members and their families have the tools and resources to vote. Absentee ballots submitted in accordance with state laws are counted for every election. People can obtain the Federal Write-In Absentee Ballot online if deployed or from their installation voting assistance officer if they did not receive their absentee ballot in time for elections. If soldiers are registered to vote while deployed and they do not get their state ballot in time to vote (45 days prior to mid-term elections) from their location, they can use the Federal Write-In Absentee Ballot found at www.FVAP.gov. They must turn it in 30 days before the scheduled election.

Academy Women: Provides programs to support and enable women from the nation's officer development programs to reach their full potential as leaders. They provide supplemental sources of education, leadership development opportunities, and resources to achieve better personal and professional balance for military women and women veterans.

Academy Women is a global leadership organization of current and former women military officers, cadets, midshipmen, candidates and all individuals committed to the success of AcademyWomen's mission. Their members are outstanding leaders to include…military officers, astronauts, pilots, combat leaders, ship commanding officers, business executives, diplomats, civic leaders, entrepreneurs and homemakers and much more. The members are the pioneers who bravely sought military training and now represent a new and outstanding paradigm of leadership.

Through a group of like-minded women and men, we will help to fill the existing gap of support by leveraging a global network; inspiring our member's ideas and action; and equipping our members for leadership impact.
http://www.academywomen.org/

Burial in a National Cemetery: Burial benefits available include a gravesite in any of our 131 National Cemeteries with available space, opening and closing of the grave, perpetual care, a government headstone or marker, a burial flag and a Presidential Memorial Certificate at no cost to the family. Some veterans may also be eligible for Burial Allowance. Cremated remains are buried or inurned in national

cemeteries in the same manner and with the same honors as casketed remains.
http://www.cem.va.gov/cem/burial_benefits/index.asp
For locations: http://www.cem.va.gov/cems/listcem.asp

Presidential Memorial Certificates (PMC): Is an engraved paper certificate, signed by the current President, to honor the memory of honorably discharged deceased veterans.
http://www.cem.va.gov/pmc.asp

Cell Phones for Soldiers: Offers FREE calling cards and SPA WAR pins to deployed service members. http://www.cellphonesforsoldiers.com/request_calling_card.php

College Financing for Veterans: Offers advice on loans, grants, scholarships and return on investment specifically for student veterans. http://www.affordablecollegesonline.org/spotlight/veterans-education-resources/

The COMMIT Foundation: Guides transitioning service members and veterans through mentorship workshops, corporate education and one-on-one transition assistance.
http://www.commitfoundation.org/

Consumer Financial Protection Bureau (CFPB) – Service Members Civil Relief Act: Provides answers to frequently asked questions and updates to the federal law. All military families need to stay updated. **Helping You Save:** Highlights resources for service members to gain financial independence. www.consumerfinance.gov/blog

Department of Agriculture – New Farmer & Ranchers Program: Offers opportunities and resources available to help veterans start a career in farming and ranching, including information on loans, grants, and where to find help and technical assistance. http://www.usda.gov/wps/portal/usda/newfarmer?navid=newfarmers **A personal favorite.**

**Department of Housing & Urban Development (HUD) –
Housing Vouchers:** Under the HUD-VASH program, combines
Housing Choice Voucher rental assistance for homeless
veterans with case management and clinical services
provided by the VA. For more information, call the National
Call Center for Homeless Veterans at 877-4AID-VET. Type in
HUD-VASH in search bar at http://portal.hud.gov.

DEERS (Eligibility Verification): www.dmdc.osd.mil/DEERS

Defense Financing & Accounting Office: www.dfas.mil and/or
(800) 321-1080

Dogs on Deployment: Provides a network for military
members to find volunteers willing to board their pets while
they are deployed or have other service commitments,
making them unable to temporarily care for their pets. Dogs
on Deployment aids pets of all types that belong to active
duty, reservists, guard, honorably discharged veterans and
their families. http://dogsondeployment.org **A personal
favorite.**

Eagle's Healing Nest: Offers temporary housing, meals,
counseling and other resources to veterans in need.
http://www.eagleshealingnest.com **A great organization
offering an inspiring new start for veterans.**

eMentor Program: Provides an information sharing,
learning and support community for veterans including
career guidance, advice, support and inspiration from more
experienced veterans, career mentors and veteran-friendly
employers. http://ementorprogram.org **Everyone needs a
mentor at some point in their life.**

F7 Group Foundation: Dedicated to serving and providing
resources, training, and support and mentoring to female
veterans and women in military families. F7 Foundation

addresses a wide range of needs for veterans in the community. Through community based collaboration, the organization brings together tools, resources, and support for veterans and military families. As the only organization of its kind and a trusted resource for those who serve, the foundation is changing lives and creating a positive community effect on our nation's future. www.F7group.com

FootStomp: Offers a social networking site connecting warrior athletes, reconditioning service members, coaches, organizations and supporters with athletic reconditioning program and events. http://footstomp.com/

The COMMIT Foundation: Guides transitioning service members and veterans (all branches, ranks) through mentorship workshops, corporate education and one-on-one transition assistance. http://commitfoundation.org

Gallant Few: Is built on the premise that transition is a new experience only to that person going through it, and that most veteran's struggle through their transitions silently, rather than admit "weakness" and ask for help. Every veteran who has successfully transitioned (sometimes after going through some lumps and bruises) has a valuable set of experiences that can help another veteran walk that same path, only this time easier and most are eager to help another.

Gallant Few facilitates this by connecting veterans with nearly similar backgrounds together in the same local area. The trust and bond between two people who have gone through the same training or served on the same ship is immediate and deep.

Two great outcomes of this are a connection to a local network that can uncover job opportunities that otherwise might not be accessible and the emotional support and friendship of another veteran.

It's difficult to connect when one comes home. None of the major veterans organizations are helping make these connections and the VA doesn't share information. This small non-profit works hard to make magic happen. The ultimate dream is that every community across the country takes seriously the responsibility to help veterans' transition home – creating mechanisms locally for veterans to volunteer to mentor, and ways for new veterans to find these mentors. Listen Tuesdays at 2pm CST at www.vetsonmedia.com/tnav POC: Karl Monger (817) 567-3293 www.gallantfew.org **This is one of my new favorite resources, they are a great support network and facilitate assistance all over the world in a quick, efficient, confidential manner.**

The Walt Disney Co. Veterans Institute/Heroes Work Here: This complimentary one-day veterans Institute program is designed to provide companies with education, examples, resources, and contacts to rapidly build and implement an effective veteran hiring program. Highlights from the day include:

*Opening & Keynote comments * Panel discussions centered around veteran hiring and resources & tools available; panelists include: Department of labor, veterans affairs, US Chamber, Joining Forces Depart of Defense and Syracuse University-Institute for veterans & military families * Veteran & Business panel: Veterans will describe their journey from the military to Disney and Disney business leaders will discuss their learning's and success in hiring veterans * Three custom-designed sessions from Disney Institute in the areas of quality service, employee engagement and leadership – all with a focus on veteran hiring * Closing keynote followed by an evening networking session * Non-profit partners and numerous government agencies presentations throughout the day with information tablets on services they provide * An evening event featuring a bit of Disney Magic Each participant will take home a specially created participant guide that compliments what they've learned and allows them to quickly establish their own veteran hiring program. **How fun is this?**

Guardian Angels for Soldiers Pet: Supports our active duty military, wounded warriors, homeless veterans, and their beloved pets to ensure the pets are reunited with their owners following a deployment related to a combat or peace-keeping or humanitarian mission or unforeseen medical and/or homeless hardship situation through various programs/services/projects. www.guardianangelsforsoldierspet.org ***I Love these organizations..they have a special place in my heart.***

Heroes At Home, LLC: Was created to help deployed military personnel celebrate, honor and stay in touch with their heroes at home. Heroes At Home believes military families are made up of two types of heroes: those who risk their lives to defend our country and those who keep households and families together while their loved ones are deployed. Services provided our: deployment coaching, gift services, military family database, deployment newsletter, blogs and forum, speaking services and a book. http://www.myheroesathome.com/blog/description/ **A resource that is new to me but looking forward to learning more about.**

Hilton Program for Job Seeking Vets: This pilot program in four states provides FREE hotel accommodations to veterans conducting job searches outside the regions where they live. Under the new Hilton Honors Program, veterans who are searching for employment, attending job interviews or skills training or looking for new housing in Minnesota, Iowa, Texas or Arizona are eligible for three FREE nights at a Hilton hotel in that state. Veterans should contact their local Disabled Veterans Outreach Program Specialist (DVOP) to be enrolled in the program. Once enrolled, veterans are eligible for 100,000 Honors points per year; for more information you can search the internet or call 800-HHONORS. ***Very Cool, Thank you Hilton for your support.***

HirePatriots.com: Do you own your own business? Starting one, looking for employment? Are you interested in hiring veterans? Do you need an odd job taken care of around the house, at the office, or at the job site? Assistance in these areas+ is the mission of this organization. HirePatriots. com which oversees projects in more than 45 states with the help of about 20 regional leaders across the country. The mission is to connect veterans with opportunities, and opportunities with veterans. If you have work that needs to be done-whether an odd job around the house , or a part-time need in a small business-individual and businesses are encouraged to post it at HirePatriots.com to help a local military member or veteran earn some extra money.

Entrepreneurs and job seekers can post capability statements, resumes, pictures, logos and other information about themselves or their companies. Great place to get the word out about your company and for homeowners to hire a veteran to complete the odd job around the house that you have been putting off. And for small business owners to get some reliable help around the office or job site for short term help. hirepatriots.com

Homes for Heroes: The purpose of this foundation is to provide and/or coordinate financial assistance and housing resources to the Heroes of our nation such as Military personnel, Police/Peace Officers, Firefighter and First Responders who are in need. www.homesforheroes.com **A personal favorite.**

Homeward Bound Adirondacks: Leads a series of trainings and retreats for veterans, professionals and community members including the veteran's reintegration academy. www.homewardboundadirondacks.org

Josephine Herrick Project (JHP) – Brooklyn VA Hospital: Offers FREE classes to veterans that promotes using photography to express their stories visually, verbally, and emotionally through hands-on work with digital cameras. http://jhproject.org/programs/veteran-administration-hospital-brooklyn/ **This is very cool, I am a huge fan and**

supporter of the arts being used to help with the healing process. I look forward to seeing more of these types of organizations.

Jewish War Veterans: http://www.jwv.org/

Justice for Vets – Veterans Treatment Court Location: Presents an interactive map of veterans Treatment Courts in the U.S. **Justice for Vets – Veterans Treatment Court Mentor Program:** Serves as model programs for individuals and court teams interested in starting a veteran's Treatment Court or for established courts interested in learning new practices. **Justice for Vets – Resources for Court professionals:** Connect your court with resources designed to support veterans Treatment Courts. www.justiceforvets.org

Justice for Vets – Veteran Mentors: Supports veterans through their readjustment to civilian life and assists them with navigating the court, treatment and VA systems. www.justiceforvets.org . ***This is gaining momentum all over U.S. look to see if it has started in your state and local area.***

Leave Recovery for Guard and Reserve Duty: Find information on the decision and administration claims procedures on restoring leave for reservists and National Guard Service Members wrongly charged leave while performing annual training or on active duty. http://www.dfas.mil/civilianemployees/butterbaughcase.html ***Very important for this community to be aware of.***

MilitaryConnection.com – Women Veterans: A website with links to a vast variety of resources for women veterans. www.MilitaryConnection.com/Women-Veterans/

Military Foster Project: PACT for Animals is a champion of the Human-Animal Bond. PACT gives peace of mind to hospital patients and military personnel by placing their pets in temporary foster homes until their owners can be reunited with the companion animals they love.

Every year thousands of companion animals are surrendered into animal shelters due to temporary crises. By providing access to safe foster homes for animals until their human companions can take them back, PACT reduces the number of animals in animal shelters and gives the owners peace of mind that their best friends (family) are not lost, abused or euthanized.

They are the ONLY active non-profit organization in the country providing this unique, essential service in the animal welfare community, and all PACT Programs are FREE. PACT carefully screen every case to find the perfect match of Foster Home and Foster Pet. Foster families stay in constant contact with the service member/hospitalized owners providing regular updates, including photos, messages and video of their pets. https://pactforanimals.org **As I stated; huge fan of these organizations.**

Military Legal Resources: Find military legal resources from the Library of Congress. Go to www.loc.gov and search for military legal resources.

Military Officers Association of America: Is the nations largest officers association with members from every branch of service, including active duty, retired, National Guard, Reserve, and former officers and their families and survivors. MOAA is a nonprofit and politically nonpartisan organization and an influential force in promoting a strong national defense. MOAA represents the interests of service members and their families in every stage of their lives and careers. For those who are not eligible to join MOAA, Voices for America's Troops is a nonprofit MOAA affiliate that supports a strong national defense. www.moaa.org or www.voicesfortroops.org

Military & Veteran Bar Association: Find links to the national and state military and veteran bar associations. http://attorneys.statelocalgov.net/state-military

Military Women in Power Ltd: Mission is to provide aid to female veterans. This organization is an All-Female veteran Task Force providing immediate emergency assistance to the veteran and their families who are desolate and despondent. They also advocate on their behalf, provide immediate resources through referrals and/or physically representing vets and their families with/to training programs, housing appointments, employment agents, completing VA claims applications, counseling MST (Military Sexual Trauma, C/PTSD (Combat/Post Traumatic Stress Disorder), Anger Management, Suicide Prevention, Parenting and Marriage counseling. They will foster support and nourish self-sufficiency for single mothers in the military for a healthy Family Care Plan if deployed. NO Membership Fee but there is a MWIP commitment to our group to "pay it forward" to another female veteran. POC: SGT Sandy Rolon, US Army (RET) 347-398-9257 MilitaryWomeninPower@gmail.com ****I have personally worked with Sandy and she is a fantastic lady with a great team beside her. She has a world of knowledge and resources at her figure tips to assist any female veteran worldwide.**

Mission K9 Rescue: Provides transportation and adoption assistance for retiring and retired military working dogs. http://missionk9rescue.org/ ****Love, love this organization!**

Music of Military Service: Operation Encore is a veteran's music project that brought singers and songwriters together to translate their military experience into song and verse. The result is a compilation CD featuring songs written and performed by active-duty service members, veterans and military spouse. The project's founders say their goal was to not only provide a therapeutic outlet for performers, but to also help bridge the civilian-military divide. The CD is currently available through iTunes and CD Baby at www.cdbaby.com/cd/operationencore. Proceeds first go toward unpaid production costs, and any profits are donated to various veterans charities and organizations. **Very impressed with this organization, I am a huge fan and look forward to seeing more from them.**

MyPay: https://mypay.dfas.mil

National Association of American Veterans: Is a non-profit designed to assist veterans in just about any way that is needed. Emergency assistance is available to veterans experiencing financial hardships in areas of mortgage/ rental, home repairs/maintenance, medical expenses and transportation expenses. They also assist with family and individual counseling to help the veteran adjust after returning from abroad. http://www.naavets.org **Great organization.**

National Association for Black Veterans: http://www.nabvets.org/

National Resource Directory for Vets: Is a federal government website that connects wounded warriors, service members, veterans, families and caregivers to thousands of service and programs at the national, state and local levels that support them during recovery, rehabilitation and reintegration. Visitors to the website can find information on topics such as post-traumatic stress disorder, military and veterans' benefits, health care, educational opportunities, homeless assistance, employment and much more. Throughout the past few months, more than 60 new resources have been added to the NRD, bringing the total number of resources that can be accessed from the site to nearly 15,000+. For more information go to www.NRD.gov. **Great resource network; they are all up-to-date and focused on areas of need.**

OutServ-SLDN: Represents the U.S. LGBT military community worldwide. Their mission is to: educate the community, provide legal services, advocate for authentic transgender service, provide developmental opportunities, support members and local chapters, communicate effectively and work towards equality for ALL. www.sldn.org ****Great to see an organization that focused on this area; it was much needed.**

Parenting for Service Members and Veterans: Delivers information and strategies to veterans and service members to improve their parenting skills through FREE online courses. Built by VA Mental Health Services in partnership with the DoD National Center for Telehealth and Technology (T2). http://militaryparenting.dcoe.mil/index.php ****Great resource and is useful to the parents of service members.**

REBOOT Workshops: The National Veterans Transition Services teaches veterans how to make social, civilian and career transitions. www.nvtsi.org

Rebuild Hope: Offers an immediate and easy way to help the OEF/OIF families. This one-of-a-kind, national network "connects" donors to beneficiaries and provide complementary services that increase the veteran's odds of success. Rebuild Hope also recognizes their personal sacrifices and efforts to rebuild their lives by sharing their personal stories. www.rebuildhope.org ****Great organization, I have worked with them and they are a great team of volunteers who are compassionate and work hard to get the job done fast, efficient and with compassion.**

Reporting the Death of a Retiree: (800) 626-3317

SaveAndInvest.org: Military-specific information for managing money, buying a home, saving for college, etc. for service members and their families. (202) 728-6933

Social Security Administration: http://www.ssa.gov

SoldierSocks: Provides veterans and service members with simple essentials needed to succeed while deployed or upon returning home. Offers care packages, basic hygienic items, help finding employment, and continuing education options.

> **SoldierSuit:** Helps paralyzed veterans receive the Ekso exoskeleton bionic suit, which enables individuals with lower extremity paralysis to walk. Units are donated to help relieve financial strain on veterans and their families.

> **SoldierScholarship:** Offers information to Operation Iraqi Freedom and Operation Enduring Freedom (OIF/OEF) and Operation New Dawn (OND) Veterans on three scholarship program available in addition to the Post-9/11 GI Bill. http://www.soldiersocks.org

Support The Enlisted Project (STEP): Provides emergency financial and transition assistance grants to active duty and recently discharged enlisted military and their families. http://www.stepsocal.org.

Team Red, White & Blue: Supports veterans and their families with physical and social activities. http://teamb.org/ ****These are great and popping up all over, jump on board and meet a great group of people.**

Thrift Saving Plan (TSP): Government – sponsored retirement savings plan for military service members (877) 968-3778.

TRICARE (Health and Dental Insurance): http://www.tricare.mil

Train A Dog Save A Warrior: Trains service dogs for wounded warriors and veterans. http://www.tadsaw.org/ ****Love, love this organization...another favorite!**

Transition Assistance Program (TAP): Updates to the program have promised the new TAP will help our service member's transition from active duty in the next four years. The foundation of the redesigned TAP is a set of career-readiness standards that are verified for ALL transitioning service members no later than 90 days prior to their separation from the military. If civilian career readiness standards are not met, service members receive further training or are referred to inter-agency partners who ensure they receive post-separation assistance. www.dol.gov/vets/programs/tap/

Troops to Teachers: Information and resources to assist service members to transition from the military to become public school teachers. http://troopstoteachers.net
I love these programs.

The United Association Veterans in Piping (VIP): Offers training and jobs in the pipe trades to veterans and active duty service members preparing to leave the service. http://www.uavip.org/veterans

U.S. VETS: Provides transitional housing, case management, employment assistance, job training and career planning to homeless Veterans. http://www.usvetsinc.org

VetCommander.com: Offers veterans face-time with their dream employer at the click of a button, delivering 60 second pre-recorded video interviews, a mobile app, and a nationwide events program that connects veterans to employers and military veteran advocates. https://www.vetcommander.com/

Veteran – Farming Programs:

Archi's Acres: http://archisacres.com/

Combat Boots to Cowboy Boots: www.start2farm.gov/programs/combat-boots-cowboy-boots

Farmer – Veteran Coalition: http://www.farmvetco.org

Vets to Ag: http://iat.msu.edu/iat/vets_to_ag

Veteran's Farm: www.veteransfarm.org

These veteran to farming programs are the most exciting organizations to come to my attention in 2014. I feel these are fabulous and will offer so much to our veterans and their families. I look forward to seeing them ALL grow and expand.

VA GI Bill: www.benefits.va.gov/gibill

Veterans in Film & Television (VFT): Provides a place in the entertainment industry for service members and veterans working or aspiring to work in the film and television a place to network with other professionals and employment. http://vftla.org/ ***Another favorite of mine!***

Veterans Loans: Covers all aspects of VA Home Loans for veterans. www.benefits.va.gov/homeloans/

Veterans of Underage Military Service (VUMS): Founded by Allan Stover in 1991 as a membership **for men and women** who circumvented age requirements in order to serve in the military; VUMS members span service from WWII to Vietnam, and at one time included WWI vets. It has identified approximately 2,800 + underage veterans, besides the opportunity to share experiences with others; VUMS strives to assure underage vets that they are protected from government retribution for falsifying their enlistment.

It is important to VUMS for the word to be shared and spread to all underage veterans to be aware they will **NOT** lose their military retirement or VA benefits for having served underage. The policy in place states if the enlistee serves until he/she is 17, than his minority time counts toward seniority and benefits. If discovered before then, underage enlistees are released with no benefits. Personal accounts of a number of VUMS members are permanently recorded in six volumes of stories titled *America's Youngest Warriors* and Dorothy Brandt, who wrote and published *America's Youngest Women Warriors* enlisted in the Women's Army Corps in February 1944 at age 16 when the age was 20. She spent 3 ½ years in the Army and shares stories of underage women. http://www.oldvums.org/ **This was very interesting to me and I was very surprised at how many were able to join during WWII and even as recently as Vietnam.**

Veterans in Construction Electrical (VICE): Provides construction and electrical case management services to qualified veterans through a program sponsored jointly by the National Electrical Contractors Association and the International Brotherhood of Electrical Workers. http://anewaop.org/programs/vice-veterans-construction-electrical/

Veterans Group Life Insurance (VGLI) Coverage: VGLI is a program that allows veterans to continue life insurance coverage after you separate from service. http://www.benefits.va.gov/insurance/vgli.asp

Veteran's Administration Women's Health Site: Provides programmatic and strategic support to implement positive changes in the provision of care for all women veterans. www.womenshealth.va.gov

VetQuest: Is a one-stop resource of college and post-military career information for transitioning veterans. VetQuest's Military Skills Transition Tool will help match the skills you have learned with compatible civilian occupations. The built-in GI calculator can show you how much assistance you have earned. VetQuest's WorkZone lets you research thousands of career options, and can guide you towards a college offering additional and relevant education. www.VetQuest.us/

VetSports: Offers programs and events helping veterans achieve better physical, mental, and emotional health through sports. http://vetsports.org **Hopefully service members will utilize this resource into their life style.**

Vietnam Veterans of America: http://www.vva.org/ **A favorite of mine. I love talking to these vets (same as the WWII veterans) as they are a world of knowledge and insight that is hard to find anywhere or with anyone else.**

Veterans Vocational Training Program: Offers veterans, their spouses and caregivers FREE vocational training in Media Arts and Video Production at Connecticut Public Broadcasting Network. http://iam.cpbn.org/

Veterans of Foreign War (VFW) – Dental Insurance: Offers information to help veterans who are VFW members select a dental plan, find rates and enroll in the MetLife Preferred Dental Program (PPD). http://www.vfwinsurance.com/veterans-dental-insurance.html **VFW a huge favorite of mine...**

Warrior-Scholar Project: Hosts a two – week workshop at top American universities to help facilitate veterans' transition from the military to college. Teaches veterans the skills they will need to succeed in college, while working to change the way they view themselves as students. http://www.warrior-scholar.org/

Warriors 4 Wireless (W4W): Connects service members and veterans with training, advanced certification and transitional support for careers in the telecommunications industry. http://warriors4wireless.com/

Workforce Opportunity Services (WOS) – VETalent: Places veterans in scholarship programs that teach them corporate, interpersonal and communication skills through a semester of classroom instruction and on-the-job training. https://www.wforce.org/

Women in Military Service for America Memorial: the memorial, at the Ceremonial Entrance to Arlington National Cemetery, is the only major national memorial honoring all women who have defended America throughout history. Their patriotism and bravery are a part of our nation's heritage and are now recognized. Visitors to the Women's Memorial experience the collective history of women in the military along with the individual stories of registered servicewomen. www.womensmemorial.org ****Great organization that I feel needs more promotion.**

Women Veterans Interactive: Wives, mothers, sisters, daughters all have served and continue to serve , but for women veterans the transition period out of the military is often difficult. Women veterans have served and sacrificed for this country but yet, after their military service is over, they find themselves suffering from major issues, like Post Traumatic Stress Disorder, Military Sexual Trauma, Readjustment Disorder, Military Related Disabilities, Low Self Esteem and other issues that often lead to unemployment, underemployment and ultimately homelessness. Women Veterans Interactive is committed to serving and supporting women veterans at their specific points of need and has created programming with this mission in mind. Programs include an Advocacy & Outreach program and a Legacy Scholarship. http://womenveteransinteractive.org/ ****Great resource for the female veteran.**

Yoga Warriors.com: To alleviate symptoms of combat stress (COSR), PTSD and increase the resilience of critical task performers working in high stress environments, including affected caregivers and family members by providing

evidence based yoga and mindfulness practices.
http://www.yogawarriors.com/ **I am a total fan and
believer of yoga...I need to incorporate it more into my daily
routine.*

Zion House: Offers female veterans' safe and supportive
housing where they have the opportunity to locate and
procure permanent housing, financial security, as well as
educational and vocational opportunities.
http://zionhouseavon.org

CAREER

**Listed are a few organizations that provide tools to assist
our veterans with facilitating employment. Remember
resumes are a top priority and need to be drafted by
someone who is familiar with the military community and
the skills you have to offer. I highly recommend using one
of the FREE resources to have yours updated or created.**

American Corporate Partners (ACP): Connects US veterans
to business leaders through mentorships and online career
advice. http://www.acp-usa.org

American Dream U: A non-profit dedicated to helping our
military get the education and access to resources they
need to find their dream job or to start a business of their
own. Check out their FREE "Dream Job" online course where
you can learn job hunting skills. http://americandreamu.org/

Boots to Business – From Service to Startup: Introduces
and trains transitioning veterans, service members, and
their spouses on business ownership through a three-step
program. http://boots2business.org/

Military Warriors Support Foundation – CEOs4Heroes:
links partnering companies and veterans in such industries
as energy, administration/clerical, business, management,
communications, customer service, skilled labor, marketing,
sales, security and more. www.militarywarriors.org

Navy Veteran Job Site: Features over 1000 career fairs
across the US; many of these events are strictly for veterans
and/or the military community. This site is FREE
www.findacareerfair.com

SAP Veterans to Work Programs: Provides training
scholarships and certification programs on SAP solutions.
www.sap.com/ms/veterans-towork.html

StreetShares.com: Works with The American Legion and
other organizations; StreetShares, Inc has launched a
new online social lending marketplace, Veterans Business
Campaign, StreetShares.com provides a new way for small
business owners to get commercial loans, funded by the
direct investments of individuals through an interactive
auction. The veterans' campaign is aimed to help military
veteran small business owners obtain commercial loans
through the StreetShares marketplace.
www.streetshares.com

Veteran Employment Center: The Veteran Employment
Center (VEC): Is an online portal that combines elements
of standard job boards and professional connection media
to provide a single solution for meeting the needs of both
veteran job-seekers and employers seeking to hire our
veterans.

The VEC is accessible from the veteran's Administration's
e-Benefits website. The VEC is open to all Reserve
& National Guard members, veterans, spouses and
dependents. The website provides job seeker access to real
job opportunities and the tools to build profiles to be shared

with employers committed publicly to hiring. It provides military skills translators to help members describe their skills and experience in terms that employers understand. https://www.ebenefits.va.gov/ebenefits/jobs

Veteran Staffing Network: Has a mission to provide their clients with top-tier talent while simultaneously reducing veteran unemployment. They provide supportive services to prepare veterans and their spouses to become job ready. They have a wide spectrum of skills sets available to clients so they are not limited to one industry and can support client needs across business disciplines. www.veteranstaffingnetwork.org

WorkForce West Virginia: Is teaming up with Hilton Worldwide to assist veterans seeking employment. Called "Operation Opportunity Initiative," the program provides hotel accommodations FREE of charge to help veterans who are being interviewed for jobs, skills training or housing searches. The program is available to veterans, current members of the military, the National Guard and reserve, and eligible spouses. Under the initiative eligible service members and veterans are awarded credits once they have registered with WorkForce West Virginia and completed an application at WorkForce office. www.workforcewv.org/

EDUCATION/SCHOLARSHIPS

Education is so important and I want our service members to be aware of the resources that are available to assist with their education decisions ALONG with the G.I. Bill. Plus these resources are available for veterans who do not have or are no longer able to utilized a G.I. Bill; again do not forget to use those scholarships that I provided in VOL I of Operation Military Resources.

ARNG Education Support Center: Contact Form: www. pec.ngb.army.mil/contact www.pec.ngb.army.mil/training/ centers/esc

Continuing Education Resources for Veterans: Learn more about resources available to veterans pursuing post-secondary education. http://accreditedonlinecolleges.org/

Cornell University Johnson Graduate School – Veterans: Presents information on intellectual, social and financial benefits for veterans considering an MBA from Cornell University. http://www.johnson.cornell.edu/

DKF Veterans Assistance Foundation: This scholarship is designed to provide financial support to California OIF/OEF veterans who are attending a California College or University. http://www.dkfveterans.com

Learn Your Why Course: This course was created by Simon Sinek, an Author, Speaker and expert on leadership and personal development. This course is geared to help you find purpose, cause, or a belief that inspires you to do what you want, need and what you do. So, if you are "stuck" in what you're meant to do in your life and career; check this FREE to veterans' course valued at hundreds of dollars. http://www.startwithwhy.com/LearnYourWhy.aspx ****Sounds like a great resource to kick start a fresh beginning.**

MAP Of Education Services Offices: To find this resource in your local area, search the title listed here with your state.

Military Education Benefits & Programs Guides: Learn about military education benefits, find degree programs and career paths, and discover the school that's right for you. www.acenet.edu/news-room/pages/military-guide-online.aspx

Military Friendly School: Includes a list of the top 15% of schools nationwide that deliver the best experience for military students. http://www.militaryfriendlyschools.com/

Military Medic to Paramedic Program: This is an accelerated program designed for veterans with Medic or Corpsman experience. LCC also offers an accelerated RN program if the veteran chooses to pursue. For more information and eligibility go to http://www.lcc.edu/nursing/militarymedic/ ***This is another of my favorites...wish it was available back in the 80's when my brother got out of the Navy.***

NG Education Incentives & Employment: www.pec.ng.mil

Online College Database: Search in this directory of online colleges and universities for information on tuition, enrollment, university type and ranking. www.onlinecollegesdatabase.org ***Great resource.***

OnlineSchool.org: A new and expanding project (2013) that allows users to search and locate all non-profit higher education intuition with online course offerings. This is a viable economical higher educational solution for individuals of all ages. Through the projects robust search function, they have created an experience that allows individuals to search and locate the nonprofit online college solution best suited to them. This is a 100% Free resource. http://onlineschool.org

Parenting for Service Members and Veterans: Offers information and strategies to veterans and service members to improve their parenting skills through **FREE** online courses. Built by VA Mental Health Services in partnership with the DoD National Center for Telehealth and Technology. http://militaryparenting.dcoe.mil

Sentinels of Freedom Scholarship Foundation: Provides scholarships to veterans and is designed to help qualified members of the US Armed Forces who were severely injured in the line of duty on or after Sept 11, 2001. (Must work a minimum of 20 hours a week). (412) 613-3855 Mr. Mark & Elaine Bozek, Team Leaders www.sentinelsoffreedom.org

Stanford 2 to 4 – A Veteran's Accelerator: Offers an eight week scholarship program that teaches student veterans and service members the academic skills needed to thrive in a competitive four-year university. http://summer.stanford.edu

Student Veteran Resources Center: The John Marshall Law School offers current and former military members assistance in applying to law school. The Student Veterans Resource Center is housed in John Marshall's Veterans Legal Support Center & Clinic (VLSC), opened its new clinic in 2013. The center brings together a staff of veterans, admission counselors, and student vets to create a support team for current and former members of the military applying to John Marshall. www.jmls.edu/admission/veterans/.

Student Veterans of America Scholarship Program: Grants scholarships to student veterans that have demonstrated academic excellence in the following categories: Critical programs commonly referred to as science, technology, engineering, and mathematics, or STEM degrees * International relations, foreign languages and diplomacy programs * other high demand fields as dictated by foundations and donors. www.studentveterans.org

The Fund for Veterans' Education Scholarship: Provides scholarships to veterans of any branch of the Armed Forces (Army, Navy, Air Force, and Marines) National Guard & Armed Forces Reserves. (507) 931-1682 or (800) 537-4180 www.afcea.org/education/scholarships/

VA GI BILL: www.gibill.va.gov/pamphlets/CH35/CH35_ Pamphlet_General.htm

65

VA Mortgage Center Scholarship: Provides scholarships to active duty military personnel, honorably discharged veterans & children of active duty military or veterans in conjunction with the Military Education Scholarship Program. www.vamortgagecenter.com/scholarships.html

Veterans Scholarship Program: Must be honorable discharged from any branch of the US Military or Coast Guard & be enrolled or about to enroll in entrepreneurial course of study. Also complete an application packet with a copy of a current resume, academic transcript, and copy of military discharge certificate, brief essay of career goal and two letters of recommendation. Go to www.enhancelives.com and click on the tab for scholarships.

Vets 4 Warriors: FREE Veteran Peer counseling 24 hours a day 7 days a week. http://www.vets4warriors.com/

GRE and GMAT Reimbursement: DANTES reimburses the GMAT or GRE general fee for eligible military personnel. Make sure you use this..even if you don't plan on going to school. The test scores are good for up to 5 years at most schools, so you don't have to worry about shelling out for the test if you decide to go later on. Worst case, you got some practice in. http://www.military.com/education/timesaving-programs/gre-and-gmat-reimbursement.html.

DANTES: "Credit by Exam" is a program that gives military personnel the opportunity to demonstrate college-level achievement through a program of exams in undergraduate college courses. http://www.military.com/education/timesaving-programs/dantes-college-credit-by-examination-program.html and/or http://www.dantes.doded.mil/educational-institutions/college-credit-alternatives/index.html

Graduate Degree Programs:

US Army War College: Program: Master of Strategic Studies www.carlisle.army.mil/

National Defense University: Colleges: College of International Security Affairs, Industrial College of the Armed Forces, Information Resources Management College, Joint Forces Staff College, National War College. http://www.ndu.edu

Judge Advocate General's Legal Center & School: Program--Masters of Law in military law http://www.jagcnet.army.mil/TJAGSA

Uniformed Services University Graduate School: Programs: Biomedical Sciences, Public Health, Nursing http://www.usuhs.mil/

Top Military Friendly Colleges and Universities: Programs: Variety of traditional and online master's degree programs. http://www.militaryfriendlyschools.com/

EQUIPMENT FOR WOUNDED & VETERANS

Finding the funds to purchase things like laptops can be a hardship at any given time but it seems we always need to purchase one at the worst or inconvenient times in our lives. I am grateful to be able to provide these resources to our service members and their families.

Laptops for Low Income: http://interconnection.org/low-cost-laptops.php

Laptops for Veterans: Are you a U.S. Military veteran or military family in need of a working laptop computer? If so, you can use the form below to request your own laptop. But first, please make sure you meet the following requirements:

Requirements for a free laptop from Laptops for Veterans: Must be a U.S. Military veteran, active-duty or reserve service member, or immediate family member (spouse or child), and be able to provide proof of service (ex. DD-214). 1. Not punitively discharged (bad conduct discharge or dishonorable discharge). 2. Understand and agree that laptops are awarded based on 1) urgency of the need, and 2) length of time on the wait list. Laptops For veterans reserves sole discretion to determine need based on the information you provide. The length of time you may have to wait depends on how many donations they have collected and how many other people are on the list ahead of you. They cannot guarantee when or if you will receive your free laptop, but we do the best they can to serve as many as quickly as possible! Further questions and application go to http://laptops4vets.org

Work Vessels for Veterans: Work Vessels for Veterans offers a hand up to returning veterans of Iraq and Afghanistan by providing the "vessel" needed to start a business or complete career education.

Work Vessels for Vets (WVFV) matches corporate and individual donations of equipment, electronics, vehicles, vessels, tools and materials with returning vets ready to start their own business.
http://www.workvesselsforveterans.org/default.aspx

Veterans4Advocacy: We are dedicated to providing free computers, software, and business start-up assistance while fostering awareness of our environment, turning used computers into opportunities for veterans and their family members. Providing veteran's information about the

opportunities available to them and essential tools to pursue those opportunities.
http://www.veterans4advocacy.org/ http://laptops4vets.org/

FINANCIAL ASSISTANCE

These resources need to be shared as many are unaware of the assistance it can and does provide. These resources provide confidential assistance; no one at the unit or base is notified of your request for assistance. Be sure to look in the Military Family chapter of this book for a list of more financial resources. And don't forget the ones listed in my first book. Make sure you ask for help...as the help is there when you need it.

Aid and Attendance Pension Program: This under-utilized and widely known program helps low income, disabled veterans receive needed medical nursing, and home care without depleting their savings. It can be used to pay for adult day care, skilled nursing care, and home care. It can also be used to pay for family member other than spouse to care for the veteran at home. This program differs from the Disability Pension provided by the US Department of Veteran Affairs. For more information you can contact your local county veteran office or visit www.va.gov. ***This is a "must" for all military to be aware of as this could be assisting many in our military community at present time.***

Coast Guard Assistance Fund: Imagine your loved one graduating from Bootcamp with no one there to celebrate with them. Our fund helps family members attend the graduation of their recruit from Coast Guard bootcamp when they could not otherwise afford to attend. 100% of your donations will help a mother, father, grandparent, spouse or sibling attend when no one else will be there. Their goal is for every recruit to be represented at graduation. This fund is a 501©3 non-profit organization and all donations are tax deductible. The fund is run by volunteers who have children in the Coast Guard. http://www.cgfaf.org/

Modest Needs: Is a national non-profit empowering member of the general public to make one-time, emergency grants to workers and veterans who are at risk of slipping into poverty. Modest Needs is proud to support military veterans through the "Homecoming Heroes Grant" a program designed to prevent our veterans from slipping into poverty as they work to make the difficult transition from overseas deployment to civilian life. https://www.ModestNeeds.org

Navy Marine Corps Relief Society (NMCRS): Provides financial assistance and education, as well as other programs and services to members of the United States Navy and Marine Corps, their family members, widows and survivors. The society also receives and manages donated funds to administer these programs and services. The Society's main goal is to help each person who comes to get support for their immediate needs. Their long-term mission is to help Sailors and Marines become financially self-sufficient by learning how to better manage their personal finances and prepare for unplanned expenses. www.nmcrs.org

HOMELESS VETERANS

It is heartwarming to see our communities coming together all over United States with non-profits and community "Stand Downs" to help solve the recurring issue of homeless veterans and their families. If you know of a family in need, please send them to one of these organizations; or even send the organization to the family.

Department of Housing & Urban Development (HUD) – Housing Vouchers: Under the HUD-VASH program, combines Housing Choice Voucher rental assistance for homeless veterans with case management and clinical services provided by the VA. For more information, call the National Call Center for Homeless Veterans at 877-4AID-VET.

Final Salute Inc.: Provides homeless female veterans with safe and suitable housing via the H.O.M.E and the H.O.P.E programs. The H.O.M.E. program provides transitional housing and subsidy assistance to homeless female veterans and their eligible children. The H.O.P.E. Program focuses on integrating veterans back into their local communities and providing vast residential areas to choose from. The H.O.M.E Program is in collaboration with many resource partners that include job placement, job training, financial planning, education assistance, and coaching. The purpose of the SAFE is to provide to all female veterans and US military reserve component service members via an interest free loan.. www.finalsaluteinc.org ****This is a great resource for female veterans.**

Homeless Emergency Project – Transitional Housing: provides affordable housing for up to 24 months to OEF/OIF and OND veterans who qualify due to low income, mental health and/or medical needs. http://www.ethep.org

Housing Assistance Programs: (800) VET HELP or contact (888) 233-8582 and/or www.nchv.org. You can also contact the VA office for the VASH Program for Housing vochers www.dvnf.org (Grants to Provide Stability Home Program)

Madison Street Veterans Association: www.madisonstreetveterans.org

Mercy Housing: www.mercyhousing.org

Military Warriors Support Foundation: Works with the Dept of Veterans Affairs and fully supports their goal of ending veteran homelessness. If you are a veteran in need, click on "contact" and write your needs or concerns. http://www.operationrenewedhopefoundation.org

National Coalition for Homeless Veterans: Resources for homeless veterans and/or veterans facing homelessness. www.nchv.org

US Department of Veteran Affairs: Provides resources for homeless veterans. www.va.gov/homeless

US Vets Inc: This nonprofit organization is dedicated to helping homeless and at-risk veterans in their effort to reintegrate to civilian life. With 12 locations across the nation and a toll free number for veterans having challenges with reintegration, this is an excellent resource. www.usvetsinc.org

United States Interagency Council on Homelessness: www.usich.gov

U.S. Vets, United States Veterans Initative: www.usvetsinc.org

Veterans Assistance Foundation: Is a non-profit dedicated to overcoming veteran homelessness. They offer programs and services for veterans from ALL branches, eras, and transitions. Go to http://vafvets.org to see a detailed list of all the resources and programs available for our military community. ****They are favorite resources of mine.**

LEGAL ASSISTANCE

Make sure you are familiar with one of these resources in the event you need legal aid. The JAG is great but they are not able to assist with civil and criminal areas in the civilian world. Plus these lawyers in many cases will even provide pro-bono assistance for the service members' immediate family members.

Military Pro Bono Project: Pro Bono legal aid for income-eligible, active duty military service members to assist with the resolution of civil legal issues; accepts case referrals from military legal assistance offices worldwide. http://www.militaryprobono.org/

LawHelp.org: Gateway to nonprofit legal aid providers and public interest law offices in each state; basic information about legal rights, self-help information, and court information, plus links to social service agencies for low-and moderate income people. http://www.lawhelp.org/

Lawyers Serving Warriors: Free legal services by volunteer attorneys to OIF/OEF service members and veterans facing administrative separation, going through a mental or physical evaluation board, or pursuing a claim with the VA for disability compensation; a project of the National Veterans Legal Service Program. (202) 265-8305 http://www.nvlsp.org/what-we-do/lawyers-serving-warriors/

National Veterans Legal Services Program: Advocacy, training, education, publications and pro bono legal assistance for veterans navigating the VA system. (202) 265-8305 http://www.nvlsp.org/

University of Detroit Mercy School of Law: If you're a veteran and could use some help, Detroit Mercy School of Law offers FREE legal assistance to veterans across the state of Michigan.

And rather than asking the veterans, many of whom have disabilities, to travel to downtown Detroit for their services, the school's lawyers and law students will make house calls using an RV-turned office. www.law.udmercy.edu (313-596-0262)

Veteran Legal Support Center & Clinic: Specializes in appealing denied veterans' benefits claims, including service-connected benefits, pension benefits, survivor benefits and education benefits. VLSC will not begin work on an initial claim that has not been filed or is currently pending before the VA. http://www.jmls.edu/

WOUNDED WARRIORS

It was hard to pick the resources to place in this area as there are many who wish to honor and support our wounded warriors.

Achilles International – Freedom Team: The mission is to enable wounded warriors with all types of disabilities to participate in mainstream athletics in order to promote personal achievement, enhance self- esteem and lower barriers to living a fulfilling life. www.achillesinternational.org ****I love this group!**

Action Trackchair: Is helping disabled veterans to be enabled. To watch amazing videos and get more information how this tool can change your quality of life, go to www.actiontrackchair.com TSS Equipment is located qt 14302 Pigeon River Road, Cleveland, WI 53015. PHONE: 888-991-3273 and the email is Sales@TssAtcSales.com ****This is an amazing tool that is bringing the control back to the veteran and changing many lives for the better. Love this product.**

Adaptive Sports Access for Wounded Warriors: Provides transportation to adaptive sports programs for wounded warriors. http://www.adaptivesportsaccess.org/

Admiral Mike Boorda Loan Program: Offers loans ranging from $500 up to $3,000 an academic year, to eligible active duty Sailors and Marines accepted to the following programs: Marine Enlisted Commissioning Education Program (MECEP), Medical Enlisted Commission Program (MECP), or Meritorious Commission Program (MCP), Application NLT 1 May. www.nmcrs.org/pages/admiral-mike-boorda-loan-program

American Music Therapy Association (AMTA): Supports organizations providing music therapy for PTSD, TBI and other emotional and cognitive issues for service members, veterans and their families. www.musictherapy.org **A totally awesome group…Love it!**

Army & Air Force Exchange Service: In an effort to support and assist severely wounded, ill, and injured Soldiers, they offer FREE alterations and modifications for this select group at all Army Military Clothing stores around the world. This Army-led initiative ensures all wounded soldiers receive FREE alterations and modifications on all issued uniforms in accordance with the Wounded Warrior Clothing Support Program to include the Army Service, Combat and Improved Physical Fitness Uniforms as well as undergarments. Eligible soldiers must present an approved Army Form 3078 along with the prescribed modifications by the physical or occupational therapist to receive free services. Learn more at https://www.shopmyexchange.com

Automobile Allowance: Service members and veterans may be eligible for a one-time payment of not more than $20,114.34 toward the purchase of an automobile or other conveyance if you have certain service-connected disabilities. http://www.benefits.va.gov/COMPENSATION/claims-special-auto-allowance.asp

Blinded Veterans Association: http://www.bva.org/

Breckenridge Outdoor Education Center Military Programs:
Hosts a series of events, camps, lessons and activities
over the course of the year for recently wounded military
personnel and veterans, and their families. Managed by the
Breckenridge Outdoor Education Center's Adaptive Ski &
Ride School. www.boec.org

Building for America's Bravest: Raises and provides funds
to build custom designed, specially adapted homes for
catastrophically injured service members.
https://ourbravest.org/

Building Homes for Heroes: Is committed to rebuilding lives
and supporting the men and women who were injured while
serving the country during the time of the war in Iraq or
Afghanistan. The organization builds or modifies homes, and
gifts them, mortgage-free, to veterans and their families.
To further assist veterans, the organization has added
programs, including financial planning services, family
funding, and emergency support.
www.buildinghomesforheroes.org ***This group has been
doing awesome work for years...love them!***

Challenge Aspen Military Opportunities (CAMO): Provides
recreational and cultural experiences for wounded warriors
with cognitive or physical disabilities in the beautiful state of
Colorado. Also provides couple retreats.
www.challengeaspen.org/military

Clothing Allowance: Veterans who have unique clothing
needs as a result of a service-related disability or injury
may receive a supplement to their disability compensation.
http://www.benefits.va.gov/COMPENSATION/claims-special-
clothing_allowance.asp ***FYI...Need to be aware of!!***

Coalition to Salute America's Heroes: Provides emergency financial assistance to severely wounded, disabled OEF/OIF veterans and their families. Categories of assistance are: mortgage/rent, home repairs, utility bills *vehicles: payments, repairs, deposits and gasoline * groceries, baby formula, and household supplies * air travel and lodging * school supplies and clothing * medical bills and co-payments. http://saluteheroes.org (914) 432-5400

Connected Warrior Foundation: Has launched an awesome program to help our veterans stay connected. This program gives 9/11 disabled veterans (combat veterans ONLY) FREE Kindles and loads of other toys. **FREE "Kindle Fire"** for disabled veterans. If you meet the eligibility requirements, follow the basic instructions and send in for your free Kindle Fire. There is also a giveaway for hospitalized veterans. www.connectedwarrior.org

Operation Google Gadgets: Ensures that every single physically-wounded warrior receives a Google Nexus tablet device for their use. The focus of this program is wounded veterans who meet the following Eligibility Requirements criteria: Combat veterans wounded physically who are resident inpatients at Walter Reed National Military Medical Center in Maryland, San Antonio Military Medical Center in Texas or the Naval Medical Center San Diego in California. Click on Programs at this link: www.connectedwarrior.org

Operation Feek's Fires: Established in honor of Navy SEAL special Warfare Operator Petty Officer 1st Class Patrick Feeks who was killed in action in Afghanistan on August 16, 2012, this program provides Kindle Fire devices to combat veterans with invisible wounds (PTSD). The distribution for this program is to a wider veteran audience, e.g. not limited to those who are resident military hospital inpatients. Go to the site for eligibility requirements. www.connectedwarrior.org/programs/feeks/

Operation Fidler's Fires: Focus of this program is the delivery of a Kindle Fire device to wounded veterans who met eligibility requirements. www.connectedwarrior.org/programs/fidlers/

IRIS Helobot Program: Is an example of this organizations effort to support wounded vets by raising awareness and support using means such as technology, both existing and innovative. Iris provides the ability for a wounded vet who is unable to travel to remotely engage and interact with people and places anywhere in the world. Iris' system works with Skype via an Android tablet, operating on a mobile platform that allows a user to be virtually present wherever the Helobot is located as it moves around and interacts with people—simply by calling Iris from a computer or phone. Good to site for eligibility requirements. http://www.connectedwarrior.org/

Cornell University – Military Community: Learn about the support and education benefits offered to wounded warriors, veterans, service members and their families at Cornell University. https://www.hr.cornell.edu

CredAbility: Is a 47 year old full service non-profit coaching agency, has formed a dedicated military coaching unit comprised of employees who are certified credit and housing counselors and have also served honorably in the U.S. military. This coaching team is complemented by veteran employees in customer service and education. These counselors have personal experience with unique situations that cause financial strain for military personnel and their families, before, during and after their tour of duty. For more information: www.credability.org

Courage Beyond at Centerstone: Provides confidential, no-cost or low-cost programs and services to warriors and their families facing PTSD and other invisible wounds of military service. They offer a supportive online community,

anonymous forums, retreats, eGroups, a 24-hour crisis line, and face-to-face counseling services.
www.couragebeyond.org

Disabled Sports USA: Offers sports rehabilitation programs, including winter skiing, aquatic sports, competition and special sports events, to anyone with a permanent disability. The Warfighter Sports Program serves wounded warriors, including those injured in the Iraq and Afghanistan wars, through sports rehabilitation programs in military hospitals and communities across the U.S. Also has a great Youth program. www.disabledsportsusa.org **LOVE THIS GROUP!!*

Disabled Veterans Assistance Program: New and returning undergraduate veterans with military-related disability who are classified as in-state and working on their first baccalaureate degree may qualify for an aid package that covers full costs without loans. Covered costs: Tuition and fees, room and board, books, personal/miscellaneous cost including the cost of a basic MSU student health insurance plan. For more information and eligibility requirements go to http://finaid.msu.edu/veterans.asp

Disabled Veteran National Foundation: Provides financial assistance in the form of a cash grant to disabled veterans. Funds can be used towards costs for housing (i.e., rent or deposit) or associated expenses such as utilities essential to operating the home (i.e., water, electricity & gas) to purchase essential food items, for travel where permanent or long-term lodging has been secured, to strengthen or expand needed services, or purchase items to improve living conditions. (202) 737-0522. http:// www.dvnf.org/

Disabled Veterans Insurance Careers: Offer job training, licensing and employment opportunities within the insurance industry for disabled veterans. http://www.dvic.us/

Disability & Veterans Community Resources Directory: Lists organizations that are available to provide assistance with training, recruiting, and hiring veterans and individuals with disabilities.www.dol-esa.gov/errd/resources and www.dol.gov

Disabled Veterans National Foundation – Grants to Provide Stability: Provides grants up to $1,000 to help eligible veterans pay for rent or mortgage or up to $500 for essential utilities such as water or electricity. www.dvnf.org

Disabled Wintergreen Adaptive Sports: Supports wounded warriors with sporting activities, special events and confidence building/mentoring activities.
www.wintergreenadaptivesports.org **The sports they offer and help with our vets is amazing...definite favorite of mine!**

Dolphin Research Center (DRC) – Wounded Warrior Project: Offers wounded warriors and their families 3 different dolphin-interaction programs in collaboration with the Wounded Warrior project's Soldier Ride, Project Odyssey and Caregiver retreat. *Military Programs:* Gives deployed service members and their families the opportunity to reconnect through dolphin recreational interactions. https://www.dolphins.org/ **I am in love with this group, I hope to visit this organization sometime in the near future.**

Eagle's Healing Nest: Offers temporary housing, meals, counseling and other resources to veterans in need.
www.eagleshealingnest.com

Embracing Wounded Florida's Heroes: Provides direct support to Florida's military veterans who have been severely wounded and disabled in Iraq and Afghanistan. Its overarching aim is to embrace these American Heroes and their families throughout their recovery and their return home as they rebuild their lives and endure associated challenges from their disabilities.
www.tamcofoundation.org

Entrepreneurship Bootcamp for Veterans with Disabilities: Offers veterans with disabilities cutting edge, experiential training in small business management to help achieve business ownership. http://ebv.vets.syr.edu/

Freedom Alliance: Provides emergence assistance for wounded troops and their families in areas of housing and travel expenses. https://freedomalliance.org/

Freedom Is Not Free: Provides assistance to combat wounded veterans and their families. Grants are provided in areas of living expenses during the transition back to civilian life, often while the veteran is focusing on recovery, rehabilitation and vocational training. Freedom Is Not Free has also renovated recovery infrastructure in the Southern CA area, including the family lounges at the Balboa Naval Medical Center, and a Concussion Clinic on Camp Pendleton. Additionally, Freedom Is Not Free hosts numerous programs in the San Diego, CA area to benefit the families of wounded or deployed soldiers. For more information go to www.freedomisnotfree.com

Guitars for Wounded Warriors: The Les Paul Foundation's Guitars for Vets helps veterans who graduates from its programs obtain guitars. The nonprofit organization enhances the lives of ailing and injured military veterans by providing them with guitars and music instruction. Through self-expression and the healing power of music; it's the organizations intent to restore the feelings of joy and purpose that can be lost after suffering trauma. For more information visit www.guitars4vets.org and/or the Les Paul Foundation at www.lespaulfoundation.org **This is such a cool idea and I am a huge fan!!**

Healing Horses & Armed Forces: Supports veterans and their families through Equine Assisted Psychotherapy (EAP) therapies designed to address symptoms of post-traumatic stress disorder (PTSD) and military sexual trauma (MST);

offers spouse and family programs.
http://www.risingmoonranch.org **I have always loved this type of healing...huge fan!!**

Healing Warriors Program: Offers alternative medicine to active duty service members and veterans for assistance with pain management and PTSD symptoms. Hosts support groups in several locations around the United States to improve the lives of the people who are caring for the wounded warriors. http://healingwarriorsprogram.org

Hearts of Valor: Honors the service and sacrifice of the women who care for our nation's wounded, Ill or injured warriors by providing a community of support based on a foundation of empathy and mutual understanding. Hearts of Valor is a network of caring people created and maintained by OHF. www.heartsofvalor.org

Helping a Hero: Offers a range of support services to service members injured during the war on terror, including mentorships that provide one-on-one advice for careers, family issues, resources, etc.., opportunities to connect with support groups for periodic, social or educational gatherings, financial assistance to cover unexpected expenses not covered by other means, opportunities to participate in sporting events, and educational grant assistance to heroes and/or their children. To learn more about any of these opportunities, call (888) 786-9531. www.helpingahero.org/ ****Great organization.**

Homes for Our Troops: Provides homes at NO COST for the severely wounded and disabled veteran or their families. An eligible veteran or service member may receive a Veteran's Administration Specially Adapted Housing Grant up to a maximum amount of $63,780. Assistance covers ALL costs to the recipient. Go to http://www.homesforourtroops.org for more information and eligibility requirements. ****Great organization.**

Hope for the Warrior: Provides guidance to wounded service members pursuing reintegration into the civilian sector. http://www.hopeforthewarriors.org/

Hope for the Warriors – Above & Beyond: Provides guidance to wounded service members pursuing reintegration into the civilian sector and much more. http://www. hopeforthewarriors.org/story/18657863/above-beyond

Hounds & Heroes: Is a totally volunteer organization that donates fully trained retired racing greyhounds as service dogs for veterans in need. Hounds & Heroes works exclusively with the greyhound breed due to the temperament of the dogs and their ability to be trained to assist the veterans. All donations to the program go toward the care of the dogs during the program – their food, vet care, heartworm meds and other necessities such as leash, collar and harness. www.houndsandheroes.com **Total fan favorite.*

K9 for Warriors: K9 is dedicated to providing service canines to our warriors suffering from post-traumatic stress as a result of conflicts and war after 9/11. www.K9forwarriors.org **Fan favorite.*

Living Springs at Lourdes – Behavioral Health Services: Offers an inpatient program to help service members, veterans and their families heal from traumatic stress and other behavioral health conditions. http://www.lourdeslivingsprings.com/

Lone Survivor Foundation: Restores, empowers and renews hope for our wounded service members and their families through health, wellness and therapeutic support. www.lonesurvivorfoundation.org

Luke's Wings: Is an organization dedicated to the support of service members who have been wounded in battle.

Recognizing the immediate need for families to be with their loved ones at such a difficult time, Luke's Wings provides families with the means to visit during the service members hospitalization and rehabilitation. By purchasing travel agency services and travel tickets for loved ones, Luke's Wings provides an immediate and invaluable service to the families of our men and women at arms while also helping to encourage and motivate the service member's recovery. www.lukeswings.org

Marines Helping Marines Foundation: They are a 501(c)3 non-profit run 100% by volunteers and have 98% of all donations received going to benefit the wounded. Started in 2003 in Maryland as a Marine Corps League Program to provide comfort, financial and material support to Marines and FMF Corpsmen in Iraq at the Bethesda Naval Hospital.

It has quickly expanded nationally to include similar support at the Brooke Army Medical Center in San Antonio, TX; the Naval Medical Center in San Diego; and the Wounded Warrior Regiments at Camp Lejeune and Camp Pendleton. Since the consolidation of Walter Reed and Bethesda, they support all services at WRNMMC-Bethesda. www.marineshelpingmarines.org ****This is a great organization which has been under the radar for too long; I hope to hear more about the great support they provide in the future.**

Military Warriors Support Program: Offers a variety of support programs and financial assistance to service members injured during active duty. Support includes educational scholarships, job retraining and placement, financial assistance in instances of pressing emergency financial situations, recreational opportunities, cost-free individual and family counseling services. Additional programs include the Host a Family program, which is designed to provide families of injured soldiers help through practical solutions and the Labrador Adoption Program, which provides a loving companion to aid in stress relief for soldiers as they decompress from PTSD, TBI and other brain injuries For more information call (210) 615-8973. http://militarywarriors.org/program

Mother Lover Fighter Sage Foundation: Find events, articles, stories and more in this foundations blog for wounded warriors, spouses and caregivers. Also offers a biannual spa day for wives of wounded warriors. http://unbridledfreedom.com/category/wounded-warriors/ ***I am new to this resource but already find it impressive.**

Musicorps: Helps wounded warriors recover from post-traumatic disorder and traumatic brain injury through music. www.musicorps.net ***Love it...fan favorite.**

One Warrior Won Service Dog Program: This Program places Service Dogs with veterans with PTSD. Depending on the needs of each veteran, these dogs may be taught to remind a veteran to take medicine, retrieve objects, or help the veteran stay calm by preventing people from crowding around them. The organization also provides education and other resources for veterans and their families about PTSD and Traumatic Brain Injuries (TBIs). www.onewarriorwon.org ***Love it...fan favorite.**

Operation Deep Down: Uses scuba diving as a tool for therapeutic and psychological value to help heal the wounded veterans. Provides training and certification for disabled veterans and their chosen dive buddy from start to finish. http://cody.sks.com/scuba_mission.aspx ***New to this resource and it sounds amazing, I can see the benefits it would have on our service members.**

Operation Family Fund: Provides emergency assistance to severely injured OEF/OIF and/or their families. Assistance provided: food, rent, utilities, emergency transportation and vehicle repair, funeral expenses, legal, medical, dental

expenses, assistance with home, rental, lease, purchase or home improvements and assistance with the purchase and rental or leasing of a vehicle.
www.operationfamilyfund.org **Great resource, I have used it to help many families.**

Operation First Response: Serves our nation's wounded warriors and their families with personal and financial needs. Services are provided from the onset of injury, throughout their recovery period and along their journey from military life into the civilian world. Financial aid varies as each case is based on individual needs ranging from rent, utilities, vehicle payments, groceries, and clothing and travel expenses. www.operationfirstresponse.org **Great resource with a timely turn around.**

Operation Homefront: Provides emergency financial and other assistance to service members, wounded warriors and their families. OH provides direct services to alleviate a military family's or individual's actual/complete emergency financial burden, as well as counseling and/or recovery support. www.operationhomefront.net (click on your state, if one not located by you-go to national for assistance). **Awesome resource which provides assistance in many was in a timely manner and with empathy and compassion.**

Operation Military Warriors Foundation: Mission is to provide support for our nations combat wounded heroes and Gold Star Families as they transition out of the military and into their new civilian life. Programs include home donation, academic and employment assistance as well as recreational activities. http://www.militarywarriors.org

Operation Proper Exit: Is sponsored by the Troops First Foundation and allows wounded warriors to return to the place where they were injured to help give them closure. One of the biggest concepts behind Proper Exit is to bring soldiers to the region where they were injured, which allows a unique type of healing and closure for the soldier that they would not have otherwise and allow them to leave the war-zone on their own terms. www.troopsfirstfoundation.org

Operation Shoebox: Sends care packages to service members overseas and wounded warriors. http://operationshoebox.com

Operation TBI Freedom: Assists veterans and active-duty military personnel with service-related traumatic brain injuries (TBI) that occurred on, or after SEP 11, 2001. http://pikespeak.co.networkofcare.org/veterans/index.aspx

Operation Ward 57: Supports wounded warriors, their families and medical staff at Walter Reed National Military Medical Center by providing items that assist in recovery, maintenance and morale. www.operationward57.org

Paralyzed Veterans of America: http://www.pva.org/

PGA H.O.P.E: Provides rehabilitation and integration for wounded warriors and disabled veterans. PGA Hope is a five week program to induce golf to enhance veteran's mental, social, physical and emotional well-being. www.pgareach.com***Awesome organization.***

Paradox Sports – Veterans Programs: Provides athletic opportunities and adaptive sports equipment with special events specifically for wounded veterans. Click on "paradox veterans" under the programs menu. http://paradoxsports.org.

PATSS – FREE Mental Health Services for OIF & OEF Veterans: Offers a range of mental health services for OIF/OEF wounded warriors, veterans, service members and their families. All services are FREE and confidential. http://www.patss.com

Pawsitive Perspective Assistance Dogs – Paw Corps: Supports veterans with skilled assistance dogs, as well as dog training opportunities (click on "pawcorps" under the "programs" menu. www.pawpads.org **Fan favorite.*

Paws4People: Through the Paws4Vets Assistance Dog Placement Program, veterans, active duty service members or their dependents with physical, neurological, psychiatric or emotional disabilities can receive Psychiatric Service Dogs, Mobility Service Dogs and Rehabilitative Assistance Dogs. https://paws4people.org **Fan favorite.*

Pets for Patriots: Provides recovery, transforms the lives of veterans, service members and wounded warriors as they adopt and care for at-risk shelter dogs and cats. Since launching in 2010, Pets for Patriots is responsible for more than 650 veteran-pet adoptions. www.petsforpatriots.org **Fan favorite.*

Project C.A.R.E. (Comprehensive Aesthetic Restorative Effort): Offers surgical and non-surgical care in an effort to improve physical appearance and restore body functions. www.DAV.org **This is an awesome organization.*

Quantum Leap Farm – At EASE Program: Provides injured service members therapeutic or recreational riding, hypnotherapy, carriage driving, and kinesthetic therapy services. The farm has "military Family Fun Day" for military families' quarterly. http://www.quantumleapfarm.org/

Real Warriors – Suicide Prevention Tools for Warriors: Defines warning signs and tools for help. For immediate help, call the Veterans Crisis Line at 800-273-TALK and press 1. You can also send a text message to 838255 to receive confidential support. http://realwarriors.net

Rebuilding America's Warriors: Learn about FREE reconstructive surgery and services available to recently wounded and disfigured service members and veterans. http://www.rebuildingamericaswarriors.com/

Resurrecting Lives Foundation: Assists veterans with Traumatic Brain Injury (TBI) by raising awareness and funding for research, treatment, advocacy and education of TBI. www.resurrectinglives.org

Ride 2 Recovery: Provides a rehabilitation experience that can impact wounded warriors lives forever. The goal is to enhance, inspire, and challenge our wounded warriors by introducing them to Ride 2 Recovery which allows each person to set individual goals while working in a group. They will partner with the local facility staff and cadre to create a personalized and progressive cycling program that fits the needs of the patient population and will promote a fuller and quicker rehabilitation. https://ride2recovery.com
***Fan favorite.**

Schoen Family Military Scholarship: Any marine combat veteran, particularly wounded veterans, are encouraged to apply for these scholarships. Must be used toward a business undergraduate or graduate degree program at the Marshall School of Business. POC: Jean Bowman (213) 740-8674 www.marshall.usc.edu

Salute Heroes: Provides disabled veterans from OIF/OEF with emergency financial aid and support services. Application and eligibility requirements are online. www.saluteheroes.org

SAVE – Statewide Advocacy for Veterans Empowerment: This new program is designed to assist veterans in need of referral services. SAVE will focus on community advocacy, suicide prevention and mental health awareness; while simultaneously identifying the issues vets are facing as they return home from service. "When your service ends, their mission begins" POC: Kevin Lambert (617) 210-5764 EMAIL: klambert@massmail.state.ma.us.

Semper Fi Fund: Provides immediate financial support for injured and critically ill members of the U.S. Armed Forces and their families. https://semperfifund.org **Great organization.**

Semper Fidelis Health and Wellness: Is a community based 501©3 nonprofit organization founded by US Marine Corps Veterans and a Holistic Health & Wellness Counselor in 2009. This team is comprised of uniquely qualified subject matter experts who deliver evidence based Holistic Integrative Health & Wellness Training and Education to Wounded, Ill and Injured Warriors, their families and care givers. Their programs focus on veterans and service members (active, reserve and veteran components) who incurred Physical or mental injury, or wounded/illness, co-incident to their military service.

This team is comprised of combat veterans, veterans' family members and some of whom sustained injuries and illnesses as a result of their service. With our diverse academic and military backgrounds, we philosophically connect with those we serve by credibly addressing their challenges. http://www.semperfidelishealthandwellness.org/

Sergeant Sullivan Center: Works to improve health outcomes for service members and veterans with post-deployment concerns through awareness, research and direct support. http://sgtsullivancenter.org/

Society of Sponsors of the US Navy Centennial Scholarship Program: Is offered to Iraq-Afghanistan combat wounded veterans who have an Associate Degree or equivalent credits and are pursuing a Bachelor's Degree or University/College courses beyond a Bachelor's Degree, leading to teacher licensure. There is NO deadline for this program, you may apply anytime. www.societyofsponsorsofusn.org

Soldier's Best Friend: Provides U.S. military veterans living with combat-related PTSD or TBI with service or therapeutic companion dogs, most of which are rescued from local shelters. The veteran and dog train together to build a trusting relationship that saves two lives at once. www.soldiersbestfriend.org ****Fan favorite.**

SoldierSocks: Provides veterans and service members with simple essentials needed to succeed while deployed or upon returning home. Offers care packages, basic hygienic items, help finding employment and continuing education options. http://www.soldiersocks.org

SoldierSuit: Helps paralyzed veterans receive the Ekso exoskeleton bionic suit, which enables individuals with lower extremity paralysis to walk. Units are donated to help relieve financial strain on veterans and their families. http://www.soldiersocks.org

Sopris Therapy – Horses for Heroes: Provides weeklong therapeutic horse riding sessions for wounded warriors. http://www.sopristherapyservices.org/

SSGT Benton Memorial Scholarship: Applicants must have served in the USMC or USMC reserve for 4 years, or two years' service and been wounded in Iraqi and honorably discharged. Must be enrolled as full-time student in any of the 23 campuses within the California State University system. https://csus.academicworks.com/opportunities/1142

Strive Recreational Therapy Services: Offers recreational therapy programs to service members and veterans with disabilities (Michigan). http://striverectherapy.com/

That Others May Live: Provides critical support, scholarships, and immediate tragedy assistance for the families of U.S. Air

Force Rescue Heroes who are killed or severely wounded in operational or training missions. www.thatothersmaylive.org

Train a Dog, Save a Warrior: The mission of Penny's from Heaven Foundation's Train a Dog, Save a Warrior Program is to unite wounded warriors, suffering with PTSD, with homeless, rescue shelter dogs, who are evaluated and deemed viable to nurture a healing and rejuvenating bond between the two. The result is a positive, non-judgmental, unconditional relationship desperately needed by both. www.tadsaw.org **Fan favorite.**

Traumatic Brain Injury (TBI): Do you feel different since returning from OIF/OEF? Are you experiencing: Memory problems, personality changes, vision problems, hearing loss, inability to concentrate, difficulty making decisions? You may be suffering from TBI.. Students with this disorder may qualify for specific learning accommodations in the classroom and also accommodate for taking tests. POC: Northwest Veterans with TBI initiative – statewide head injury program at (617) 204-3852 or www.biama.org

USA Together: Connects injured service members and their families with donors willing to provide support or financial assistance. http://www.financialhelpresources.com/details/usa_together_inc.html

U.S. Vets – Barbers Point: provides transitional housing, case management, employment assistance, job training, and career planning to homeless veterans. http://www.usvetsinc.org/barberspoint/

VA VOC Rehab Buys Disabled Veterans iPads & More: This is another one of those hidden gem's for military families. The VA can assist with purchasing programs for high tech items for veterans. By learning who to ask and the eligibility requirements hopefully I can help some disabled veterans get the equipment they need to help with their recovery and succeed. In reality, there are many different programs the VA manages within the Health Administration and Benefits Administration. Different rules apply to the VBA and VHA, but the VA is not clear about specifics as to how to qualify. http://www.disabledveterans.org/2012/01/19/va-buys-disabled-veterans-ipads-and-more/

Veteran Counseling Centers: Check the website to find a center in your area. These centers are run by combat veterans. http://www.vetcenter.va.gov/ or call 800-905-4675.

Vets Access, LLC: Is a General Contractor Company that specializes in independent living for the community. They offer full realm of services to assist people wishing to live independently and age in place. Offers:: home modifications, ramps, DME (durable medical equipment), HME (home medical equipment), ramp rentals. They are a registered SDVOB (service disabled veteran owned business) and are C.E.A.C. (certified environmental access consultants) which certifies them as qualified specialists in accessible home modifications and independent living solutions, complete design specifications, building, remodeling,, code compliance consulting, ADL (activities of daily living) assessments and aging-in-place needs. www.vetsaccessllc.com,

Veteran – Direct Home and Community – Based Service Program: This program helps provide home and community based support services that help older or disabled veterans remain living safely and independently in their own homes for as long as possible. www.region3b.org click on "resources" then "veteran"

Vets Journey Home (VJH): Is an all-volunteer organization that helps with the emotional healing of service members. VJH started in 1989 as Bamboo Bridge to work on the emotional healing of Viet Nam Vets. In 2004 the name was changed to include all active duty, reserve and veterans, all service times and all branches of service. All retreats are FREE to service members. They are located in Wisconsin, Maryland, Pennsylvania, Florida, Texas and California. The volunteers are veterans and civilian family members of vets, reserves, or active duty. The weekend retreats are put on to assist participants with unloading the emotional baggage they carry due to experiences in service to our country. www.vetsjourneyhome.org

Veteran Love and Appreciation: Provides emergency assistance for severely wounded and disabled OIF/OEF veterans in areas of food, gas and emergency travel. www.veteranlove.com/

Veterans Vocational Rehabilitation: Veterans may be eligible for Voch Rehab (chapter 31 benefits) if they have received a discharge under other than dishonorable conditions, incurred or aggravated a service-connected disability whether physical or psychological (10% disability or higher). If approved for this benefits, students will receive full tuition & Fees, book voucher, substance allowance, counseling, medical, dental & Optical coverage, support services, tutoring and job placement services once program is completed. Find the link by searching for Veterans Vocational Rehabilitation.

Walleyes For Warriors (Michigan): Is an annual fishing event supported by Operation Injured Soldiers (OIS). OIS is a 501c3 non-profit organization operated by volunteers that stand by our injured veterans. They believe that many injured vets have suffered very traumatic injuries while serving our country, some physical and some hidden deep inside. They offer our vets a chance to do the things that they thought was no longer possible after their injuries, such as hunting, fishing, and sporting events. With specialized hunting equipment, they can send amputees in the fields for hunts, with donated fishing boats and captains, they also take vets fishing (event held in June) POC Nels Larsen 989-928-4368.

www.walleyesforwarriors.com **This is a great yearly event that bring an awesome community together in support of our veterans. The turnout of vets, vendors and military families is breath taking.**

Warrior Canine Connection: Provides opportunities to veterans with post-traumatic stress disorder or traumatic brain injuries to train service dogs for other veterans. http://www.warriorcanineconnection.org **Awesome organization and opportunity for veterans.**

Warriors To Work Program: Through WWP encourages veterans entrepreneurship and warriors to work. FOR WARRIORS—The Warriors to work program provides career guidance and support services to WWP Alumni interested in transitioning to the civilian workforce. They will match your skills and experience to the needs of hiring managers. These services are also open if you are registered with Family Support, Our specialists can help in area of: Set attitude goals, build an effective resume, Prepare for an interview, Network with local sample. And much more. http://www.woundedwarriorproject.org/mission.aspx

Wasatch Adaptive Sports – Veteran Programs: Offer veterans with special needs outdoor therapeutic recreational and social activities to promote healing in a safe and natural setting. http://wasatchadaptivesports.org/veterans/ **This is a new one for me and looks very interesting.**

Wintergreen Adaptive Sports: Supports wounded warriors with sporting activities, special events and confidence building/mentoring activities. http://wintergreenadaptivesports.org/

Women Army Corps Veteran Association: Promotes the general welfare of all veterans, particularly the personnel of the Women's Army Corps, its veterans and veterans of the Women's Army Auxiliary Corps, in hospitals or wherever the need exists; to provide publications pertaining to the members; to further general education and civic interest programs for the betterment of the community.

Provides support to WAC Museum and Hospitalized Writing Project, scholarships, maintenance of the women's army corps veteran redwood memorial grove along with hosting social functions. http://www.armywomen.org/

Women Veterans Health Program: Promotes the health, welfare and dignity of women veterans, and their families, by ensuring equitable access to timely, sensitive, quality health care. The program provides a full range of medical and mental health care services, including: Primary care, Gynecology services, patient education, productive health screening, including breast cancer, cervical cancer and osteoporosis, screening, counseling and treatment for sexual trauma, substance abuse, PTSD and domestic violence, vocational rehabilitation, homeless programs and research. www.womenshealth.va.gov

Wounded Warrior Regiment: Is the official command charged by the Commandant of the Marine Corps to provide longitudinal care and support for wounded, ill and injured Marines and their families. They provide leadership and enables non-medical care to combat and non-combat Wounded, Ill and injured (WII) Marines, sailors attached to Marines units, and their family members in order to maximize their recovery as they return to duty or transition to civilian life. http://woundedwarriorregiment.org

RETREATS FOR WOUNDED WARRIORS

All these retreats look and sound amazing and offer a wonderful opportunity for the service member to go and heal and relax in a non-threating environment with others who understand and can help you on the path of growth and healing. Each has its own special tools and services. Remember it is not required for veterans to be a resident of the state in order to participate in these retreats.

Boulder Crest Retreat: Provides a rural retreat for wounded, ill, and injured service members and their families to reconnect, recover and reintegrate through sports and retreats. http://bouldercrestretreat.org/

Compass Retreat Center: www.compassretreatcenter.org

Courage Beyond at Centerstone: Offers retreats and services to warriors and their families facing PTSD and other invisible wounds of military service members. www.couragebeyond.org

F.I.S.H. Fishermen in Support of Heroes: www.fishheroes.org

Flyin' Heroes: Is a program that utilizes the sport of fly fishing to promote therapeutic growth and rehabilitation of U.S. military veterans. The goal of Flyin Heroes is to create memorable fly fishing experiences that unlock the healing power of the water and foster lasting relationships. www.flyinheroes.org/

Healing Warrior Hearts: Offers retreats for military personnel, veterans and their families which emphasize communication, reintegration and healing from war. http://starfishfound.org/veterans/

House in the Woods Inc.: http://www.houseinthewoods.org

Hunters Helping Soldiers: www.huntershelpingsoldiers.org

Samaritan's Purse and Operation Heal Our Patriots:
Gives 150 wounded veterans and their spouses spiritual
engagement opportunities through retreats and recreation.
Lodging and transportation included.
http://samaritanspurse.org/

Serve Our Willing Warriors – Bull Run Retreat: Offers
recovering wounded, ill and injured warriors and their
families a break from the hospital environment to relax in a
peaceful weeklong retreat. http://www.willingwarriors.org/

Soldier's Heart: Offers holistic healing retreats, international
reconciliation journeys, training and public education for
service members, veterans and their families affected by
post-traumatic stress disorder (PTSD), View website for list
of contacts who work with Soldier Hearts.
http://www.soldiersheart.net

Songwriting with Soldiers: Conducts small weekend retreats
that pair professional songwriters with active-duty service
members and/or veterans to turn combat and transition/
reentry experiences into songs.
www.songwritingwithsoldiers.org

Team River Runner (TRR): TRR is an all-volunteer
organization run by a council of kayakers and overseen
by a board of directors. Working in partnership with The
Wounded Warrior Project and Disabled Sports USA, TRR
helps veterans of the Iraq and Afghan wars recuperating at
Walter Reed Army Medical Center (WRAMC) find health,
healing, and new challenges through whitewater boating
on the Potamac River.While the focus of TRR's work is
on soldiers recuperating at WRAMC, TRR also provides

whitewater boating opportunities for family members as well as for other wounded warriors.
www.teamriverrunner.org

Warriors & Quiet Waters Foundation: Offers a six day program of fly fishing and recreation in Montana to injured service members from Iraq and Afghanistan.
http://warriorsandquietwaters.org

They have wielded the sword of Patriotism for their country and now have transformed it into a pen to write marvelous stories. Join this creative group of women warriors who are also creative authors and a therapeutic supportive unit for each other.

Romvets began when former military women, Merline Lovelace and Lindsey McKenna got together for a drink at the Romantic Times convention in St. Louis in 2002. Since then this group has expanded to over 170+ members (13 still active duty) with 1600+ years served and over 1300+ book titles sold. Members have received national recognition and awards in every category and genre written.

ROMVETS are female veterans and writers. Each woman is either an aspiring writer or a published author. Because they are teamwork oriented, they trade information easily and with trust among the members. This trust comes directly from their military service and indoctrination.

As a result, the members are free to share their publishing experiences, agent information, and all different facets of what a writer needs to know to successfully negotiate the publishing realm. Plus the healing aspect of sharing their life struggles and growth as writers is priceless. RomVets rave with joy when one of their vets gets published or when one makes it on a vaunted list, such as the New York Times Best Seller or USA Today list. And they shriek with delight when one of their vets wins a major award at RWA. Which is a lot...you will be amazed at the names on this list... If you are a female veteran and would like some assistance and insight join ROMVETS...this is a FREE Organization full of a bunch of fabulous, creative, insightful ladies. www.RomVets.com

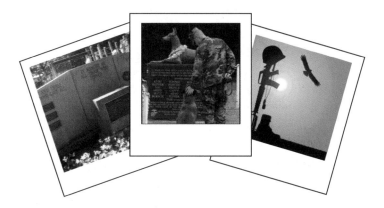

DECEASED VETERAN

Death is never an easy subject to discuss or plan for in advance. And it is very hard to accept when it is unexpected and/or your loved one passes while away from home. Families are left with a feeling of "no closure," especially for military families who are expected to be structured and plan for the future and the unexpected. I hope these resources can offer you peace of mind in your time of need.

A Survivors Guide to Benefits – Taking Care of Our Own: This guide is intended to aid you as you work through the difficulty and pain of losing a loved one who was serving in the military. http://www.militaryhomefront.dod.mil/

American Fallen Soldiers Project: The American Fallen Soldiers Project was formed to help provide comfort and healing to the mourning families of our fallen military men and women. With a mission to honor, respect and forever memorialize those who have sacrificed their lives while protecting our freedom. They provide, at no cost an original portrait of their fallen loved one that fully captures their appearance and personality.
http://www.americanfallensoldiers.com/ **Beautiful...**

American Gold Star Mothers: Resources for parents who have lost their child in a time of war. http://goldstarmoms.com ** *An amazing group of families...*

American Widow Project: This non-profit was launched in 2008 by Taryn Davis who became a widow at the age of 21 years. It is dedicated to the newest generation of war widows, including some who lost their spouses to non-combat causes with an emphasis on healing through sharing stories, tears and laughter. The organization has a camaraderie that their spouses had and their hotline is staffed with fellow widows, not by grief counselors. Official events include surfing and skydiving rather than speakers and seminars. This is an organization that strives and encourages each other with hope for the future. http://www.americanwidowproject.org/

Bereavement Counseling for Surviving Family Members: Support to loved ones who suffer with emotional/psychological stress after the death of their loved one. It includes a broad range of transitional services, including outreach, counseling, and referral services to family members. www.vetcenter.va.gov/bereavement_counseling.asp

Burial Flags: A United States flag is provided, at no cost, to drape the casket or accompany the urn of a deceased veteran who served honorably in the U.S. Armed Forces. It is furnished to honor the memory of a veteran's military service to his or her country. http://www.cem.va.gov/burial_benefits/burial_flags.asp.

Fallen Patriot Fund/The Mark Cuban Foundation: Was established to help families of US Military personnel who were killed or seriously injured during OIF/OEF. http://fallenpatriotfund.org

Fannie Mae Military Forbearance Option: If you're facing a financial hardship due to a death of injury of a service member on active duty, you may be eligible for a special military forbearance option. Forbearance is an agreement between you and your mortgage company to temporarily suspend or reduce your monthly mortgage payments for a specific period (usually between 90-180 days) of time. This option lets you deal with your short-term financial problems by giving you time to get back on your feet and bring your mortgage current.

With a military forbearance, you may qualify for additional benefits such as longer forbearance period – up to six months – and no adverse impact to your credit score (all credit reporting related to your mortgage loan will be suspended during the forbearance period). Additionally, a special hotline has been set up for additional guidance about this option and other mortgage assistance programs—877-MIL-4566 www.knowyouroptions.com

Government Headstones or Markers: For an unmarked grave of any deceased eligible veteran in any cemetery around the world, regardless of their date of death provided by the VA. http://www.cem.va.gov/hmm/

Hero's Rock: Is a non-profit that builds custom tribute rockers for the children of fallen heroes. Each rocker is created to honor each hero's line of service, has etched portraits of the hero along with their service medallions and their service title engraved in the bottom. These rockers are a comforting toy for the child at their time of loss and later an heirloom to remind them of their loved one and that our nation appreciated the great sacrifice these men and women make for their country. http://www.herosrock.us/ ****These *rockers are very beautifully made and with deep respect for the families. This is one organization I am very glad came to my attention. Great Job!***

Snowball Express: Every day, many of the men and women of the armed forces return to their families and their civilian lives. But not everyone will have that chance and the families left behind are forever changed. Snowball Express remembers those fallen heroes who will never return and honors the sacrifice their families have made by serving the children who will never be reunited with their mom or dad. www.snowballexpress.org

The Marine Corps Causality Assistance Program: Has signed a Memorandum of Agreement with TAPS, which allows closer coordination between the groups. Together they will provide comfort and care to anyone who has suffered the loss of a military loved one, regardless of the relationship to the deceased or the circumstances of the death. For more information go to www.marines.mil and click on the link for "causality assistance."

Military Assistance Program Central: Assistance with Casualty and Mortuary Affairs. www.dvnf.org

The Matthew Freeman Project: Is a not-for-profit charitable organization dedicated to the support of education in order to promote communities of promise, prosperity and peace throughout the US and the world. Their mission is to help Gold Star Families deal with their grief. "Matthew Bears" was created from the uniforms of those Killed in Action, killed in training or who have died as a result of the wars. The Captain Matthew Freeman Gold Star Sibling Scholarship was established in memory of Captain Matthew C. Freeman, USMC and to honor his beloved sisters, Marybeth and Virginia. It is to acknowledge the struggles and emotional pain when dealing with the loss of a sibling through a combat related death. www.freemanproject.org

The Survivors of Service Members SOS Fund: Provides funds to families who have lost a loved one in Iraq. http://sosfund.us/mission.htm

Tragedy Assistance Program for Survivors (TAP): Provides for the families of a fallen service member. It offers support groups, seminars, grief camps and other resources. Since families of suicide victims are often affected differently from families of service members fallen in combat, TAPS developed programs and events geared directly for this group. http://www.taps.org or toll free crisis line at 800-959-TAPS.

Veterans of Foreign Wars (VFW): Great emergency assistance and resource during this time of need. http://www.vfw.org/

THE BEST THING IN LIFE IS
FINDING SOMEONE WHO
KNOWS ALL YOUR FLAWS,
MISTAKES AND WEAKNESSES
BUT STILL THINKS
YOU'RE COMPLETELY AMAZING

MILITARY SPOUSE

Over the years I have found it frustrating and sad when I hear the stories or speak with another spouse regarding their hardships. In a society where we have so much technology and networking NO service member or their family should be suffering or struggling in anyway alone. As a strong community we need to be aware, up-dated on benefits and share among each other.

With that said...There are many great resources available for military spouses in all areas of need. Please take the time to look through all the new ones listed (make sure you go through the resources in my first edition as well) plus the added social networking sites for you to connect with other military spouses from all over the world.

Abandoned Military Spouse: U.S. Military Officials a few years ago started the this hotline in hopes of helping women left stranded, both intentionally and un-intentionally by their service members/husbands. This has become a rising problem in overseas countries like Korea. This is illegal and should not be tolerated. Please call the hotline if you or someone you know is in this situation at 505-730-3635. And leave a message in one of five different languages; English, Korean, Spanish, Russian, or Tagalog. officials are hoping to

spread the word so military personnel will realize they can no longer continue this behavior to their families.
www.stripes.com/abandoned and
www.facebook.com/abandonedamericanmilitaryspouse

Air Force Enlisted Village: Founded in 1967 to provide a safe, secure and dignified place for indigent surviving spouses of retired Air Force personnel. The Village's primary goal and focus is to provide a home and financial assistance to these women. The surviving spouse with the greatest need is cared for first and none are refused assistance due to financial status. Low pay and frequent military moves leave some spouses without careers, home equities, retirement plans or any significant assets. Surviving spouses requiring financial assistance live here among peers sharing memories of Air Force life without the stigma normally associated with subsidized housing facilities. http://afenlistedwidows.org/

American Widow: Is dedicated to the newest generation of war widows, including some who lost their spouses to non-combat causes with an emphasis on healing through sharing stories, tears, and laughter. The organization has a camaraderie that their spouses had and their hotline is staffed with fellow widows, not by grief counselors. Official events include surfing and skydiving, rather than speakers and seminars. This is an organization that strives and encourages each other with hope for the future.
http://www.americanwidowproject.org

American Military Partner Association: Their mission is to connect, support, honor and serve partners and spouses of America's LGBT service members and veterans.
www.militarypartner.org

Army Wife Network: Is an interactive website with blogs, columns, radio shows and plenty of answers to your military life-related questions. http://www.armywifenetwork.com/

Army Wife Network is a great group of ladies working hard to provide useful information, resources and tools for our military community.

Battling Bare: Provides a network of great support for the military spouses, their children and other family members who silently struggle to carry the burden of assisting those who struggle with PTSD. www.battlingbare.blogspot.com ***This is a new organization that came to my attention in 2014...I am very impressed and look forward to seeing more from them in 2015.***

Brides Across America: Making dreams come true by giving a military bride a FREE wedding gown during a Brides Across America's Nationwide Gown Giveaway. Events are held twice a year in partnership with bridal salons across the country. http://www.bridesacrossamerica.com/about.html

Blue Star Families: This non-profit is committed to supporting one another through the unique challenges of military service and asking the larger civilian population to help as well, connecting military families regardless of rank, branch of service or physical location, and empowering military family members to create the best personal and family life possible for themselves. http://www.bluestarfamilies.org/

Christian Military Wives: is a branch of Christian Military Fellowship, and produces https://www.cmwives.org and http://www.facebook.com/christianmilitarywivesfellowship

Faith Deployed & Faith Deployed Again: Created by Jocelyn Green, a Coast Guard wife to assist military spouses (and others) who wished to grow spiritually and assist each other during deployments. Provides a great resources listed on her site. www.faithdeployed.com **Jocelyn is an amazing woman who provides encouragement to women all over the world. Her website is a "must" for all military spouses.**

Military Spouse

109

Marine Wives: Informative site for Marine wives. http://marinewives.com

Military MOPS: Mothers of Preschoolers (MOPS) has a group just for military wives. http://www.mops.org/

Military Spouse Corporate Career Network: Focuses on Employment Readiness, Training Programs, Job Placement Solutions and No-Cost Services to all military affiliated spouses, retired military spouses and caregivers to wounded warriors. http://www.msccn.org/

Military Spouse Magazine: Is a wonderful magazine created for the military spouses. The magazine and online site provides helpful websites, creative ideas, resources and more to their readers. www.milspouse.com

Military OneSource: This is a great resource website; it offers education, health, relocation, parenting, stress---you name it and they provide links. Available by phone or online, their FREE service is provided by the Department of Defense for active duty, Guard/Reserve and their families. The service is completely private and confidential, with few exceptions. http://www.militaryonesource.com/MOS.aspx

Military Spouse Employment Survey: Provided a platform for all military spouses to share their personal challenges of employment while trying to navigate the military lifestyle. http://www.moaa.org/milspousesurvey/

Mother Lover Fighter Sage Foundation: Find events, articles, stories and more in this foundation's blog for wounded warriors, spouses and caregivers. Also offers a biannual spa day for wives of wounded warriors. http://unbridledfreedom.com/category/wounded-warriors/

Naval Services FamilyLine: Is the source for Sea Service Spouse Mentoring. This non-profit is dedicated to empowering ALL Navy, Marine Corps and Coast Guard families to meet the challenges of a military lifestyle. NSL FREE training materials and programs are available to all spouses and family members around the world and have been helping families for nearly 50 years in all stages of their sea service lives. www.nsfamilyline.org

Operation MOM: A support group and a site full of resources for families of all branches of service. http://www.operationmom.org/

Operation R.O.S.E: The VISION of Operation R.O.S.E. is to personally connect with our military sisters and help them get connected at their new duty station. They strive to create an intimate environment within their connect groups where she can feel safe knowing her privacy is protected, she will never be judged and Operation R.O.S.E will always nurture her... especially through challenging situations. Their MISSION is to establish "Connect Groups" for women on or near every military base around the world where they can personally reach out, support & encourage their sisters to establish a closer walk with Christ. And to equip them with strength & courage while learning how to stay connected after a PCS (Permanent Change of Station). http://www.operationrose.com/index.html

Patriot Guard Riders: Attends memorial and funeral services for service members killed in action and honorably discharged veterans to shield the family from interruption created by protestors. www.patriotguard.org ****This group is amazing and way under appreciated. They do so much volunteer work and fundraisers. I wish they would get more recognition.**

Spousebox.com: Care packages for military spouses by military spouses. http://thespousebox.com

Spouse Mentoring (COMPASS): COMPASS is a standardized Team-Mentoring Program Development by Spouses for Spouses. COMPASS focuses on spouses new to the Navy, however; all spouses are welcome. COMPASS improves quality of life through education, enabling, and spouses to understand, experience and meet the challenges of the Navy lifestyle. With this knowledge and realistic expectations, their journeys can be successful and rewarding. http://www.gocompass.org/

Support the Enlisted Project (STEP) – Wounded Warriors Caregiver Support: Organizes and hosts events for the wives of our wounded service members to relax, rejuvenate and reconnect with other caregivers in similar situations. http://www.stepsocal.org

Uniformed Services Former Spouses Protection Act: The name of this site speaks for itself. This is important information to know. http://www.military.com/benefits/retiree/unifirmed-services-former-spouses-protection-act.

Vietnam Veterans Wives: Offers counseling and assistance with VA filings, Chapter 35 benefits filings and burial benefits. http://www.vietnamveteranwives.org/

Wives of Faith (WOF): Encourages spiritual growth in all military wives as they pursue Christ as the center of our lives. This is a place of refuge and peace, a place where as wives; you can find connections with others and grow in your walk with God as you experience the joys and challenges of military life and as women. This group wants to see you grow in your relationship with God. And in turn, know that your relationship with Him will impact your relationship with your husband and your kids and other military spouses.

Rank is left at the door and emotions are shared as you work towards being empowered; not on your own strength but by God's strength, finding hope and helping others find the hope we know in Jesus. Offered online Bible studies are based off books written by Sara Horn. "Tour of Duty: Preparing our Hearts for Deployment," is specifically for military wives with deployed husband. She also has a "Military Wives Spiritually Survival Guide" encourages military wives to lean on God for support and strength. http://www.wivesoffaith.org/

EMPLOYMENT

I have a couple of great new resource sites for employment. Don't forget the resources in my first edition as well. Is there one you think is better or should be listed? Email me: Kim@MilitaryResourceBooks.com

Milspouse: Is a support site to assist military spouses with their unique and challenging lifestyle. In the past Milspouse has assisted with careers such as nursing or education but they have greatly expanded and even assisted with home business information that works more easily within the military lifestyle. www.milspouse.org

Military Spouse Career Network: Provides an employment program created by a military spouse and operated by military-affiliated MSCCN Team members. The MSCCN is dedicated to providing career opportunities and job portability for military spouses through a nationwide network of employers. http://www.mscn.org

Boots to Business – From Service to Startup: Introduces and trains transitioning veterans, service members, and their spouses on business ownership through a three-step program. http://boots2business.org/

CareerOneStop: Site offers career resources and workforce information to job seekers, students, businesses and workforce professionals to foster talent development in a global economy. Go to http://careeronestop.org and www.careeronestop.org/militaryspouse/

Career Spark: Walks military spouses through a developing a resume based on their unique skills and makes their resumes searchable to thousands of employers. Provided by the U.S. Chamber of Commerce's Hiring Our Heroes Program. http://www.mycareerspark.org

Dependency & Indemnity Compensation: Is monthly benefit paid to eligible survivors of a: Military service member who died while on active duty, or veteran whose death resulted from a service – related injury or disease, or veteran whose death resulted from a non-service related injury or disease, and who was receiving, or was entitled to receive VA Compensation for a service-connected disability that was rated as totally disabling for at least 10 years immediately before, or since the veteran's release from active duty and for at least five years immediately preceding death, or for at least one year before death if the veteran was a former prisoner of war who died after September 30, 1999.

The surviving spouse is eligible if he or she: Validly married the veteran before January 1, 1957, or was married to a service member who died on active duty, or married the veteran within 15 years of discharge from the period of military service in which the disease or injury that caused the veteran's death began or was aggravated, or was married to the veteran for at least one year, or dad a child with the veteran, and cohabited with the veteran continuously until the veteran's death or, if separated, was not the fault for the separation, and Is not currently remarried

A surviving spouse, who remarries on or after December 16, 2003 and on or after attaining age 57, is entitled to continue to receive DIC. DIC benefits may be paid to the veteran's minor surviving child or children, but only where there is no surviving spouse. Whenever applicable, the children will be paid in equal rates set by statue. For more information go to www.benefits.va.gov

InGearCareer.org: Is a non-profit organization created by military spouses for military spouses past and present. In Gear Career provides a FREE forum for professional development, community support, information sharing and networking to address the unique challenges faced by career-minded military spouses. www.ingearcareer.org

Medical Transcriptionist: Another portable career choice for military spouses because of the nature of the work. Most of the data is submitted electronically, so you can work from anywhere. There are educational requirements associated with the field, but there are many schools that offer military spouses discounts for this field of study. For more information in this field, you can go to www.careerstep.com and follow the link for job.

EDUCATION/SCHOLARSHIPS

This is one of the best (in my opinion) resources for military families. Education is so expensive and the assistance and generosity of these scholarships can be a life saver.

AFCEA General Emmett Paige Scholarships: Provided for persons on active duty or their spouses. www.afcea.org/education/scholarships/undergraduate/ EmmettPaige.asp

AFA (Air Force Association) Spouse Scholarships: For spouse of Air Force active duty or Air Guard or Air Reserve. www.afa.org/home

American Association of University Women: Offers scholarships for women and are awarded to eligible women who meet the specific requirements of AAUW Branch and State offices. http://www.aauw.org

Army Emergency Relief Spouse Education Assistance Program: Only for dependent Spouses of active duty soldiers assigned to Korea, Japan, Okinawa, or Europe. http://www.aerhq.org/dnn563/EducationalAssistance.aspx

Blinded Veterans Association (BVA): Provides scholarships to spouses of legally blinded U.S. Forces veterans. http://www.bva.org

Bowfin Memorial Scholarship: For members of the Hawaii submarine forces personnel and their family members. Email: dcpcc@aol.com

Coastline College Military Spouses Program: Provides reduced tuition rate and FREE textbooks for degrees offered entirely online. www.military.coastline.edu

Command Spouse Leadership Course (CSLC), Newport RI: This course is an officially funded Navy course which focuses on building an effective commanding officer/spouse team. It provides the dedicated time and tools for the couple to discuss, prioritize, plan, and formulate their personal Command Tour Charter. That charter should reflect each other's goals and expected participation in all facets (professional and personal) of the command tour. www.nsfamilyline.org

Continuum Training Modules: Naval Services Family Line has created this page to highlight the spouse education training modules developed to assist the Navy spouses in various areas including: communication, CO/XO spouse education, crisis management, deployment/support groups, entertaining with ease, etiquette and protocol, and spouses mentoring. www.themovingwell.com

Dr. Jack Callan Memorial Scholarship: Saint Leo University. Spouse must have 9 credits minimum to qualify. http://www.saintleo.edu

Fleet Training Center Petty Officers Association Scholarship Fund: For spouses of a living or deceased past or present staff member of the FTC Norfolk. www.cposf.org/

Folds of Honor Scholarship: Offers college scholarships for spouses and children of service members disabled in action or killed in action in Iraq or Afghanistan. Applications may be submitted in advance for children who will not need the scholarship for several years. Scholarship amounts are determined on a case-by-case basis. http://www.foldsofhonor.com/scholarships

Hope for the Warriors: Offers multiple scholarships to U.S. military spouses of wounded service members and Fallen Warriors. http://www.hopeforthewarriors.org/story/18727849/spouse-caregiver-scholarships

Joanne Holbrook Patten Military Spouse: This is for military spouses who are pursuing a GED, certificate program, or undergraduate or graduate program that will lead to meaningful employment. Spouses or retirees and survivors are also eligible. (703) 931-6632 www.cofc.edu

Marine Corps Air Station Officers Spouse Club (Parris Island): Contact Mary E. DeWolfe (843) 379-9654.

Military Spouse Scholarship from Home Depot: Offers a $10,000 scholarship yearly to a military spouse. http://militaryspouse.com/education/orangehonors13/

The National Institute of Whole Health: Is offering a $1,250 scholarship to all qualified MyCAA participants, toward their enrollment in an NWH Whole Health curriculum. http://www.wholehealtheducation.com/

The National Military Family Association Scholarship Fund: Awards scholarships for military spouses. Applications, when available are posted on their website. http://militaryfamily.org/

The Navy Wives Clubs of America: Offers a scholarship program for spouses of enlisted Navy, Marine Corps, and Coast Guard members. http://navywivesclubofamerica.org/

Non-Commissioned Officers Association (NCOA) Scholarship Grant: For spouses of members of NCOA. www.ncoausa.org

Parris Island Officers Spouse Club: Contact Rebecca Varicak (843) 522-1615

Parris Island Staff Non-Commissioned Officers Spouse Club: Contact Joanne Bright (843) 525-1756.

Park University Military Family Scholarships: Used at home campus in Park, MO or at the Beaufort, SC Campus Circle. Contact (843) 228-7052

Protect and Serve Grant: Scholarship awarded to spouses of U.S. military from Peirce College, up to 25% on tuition fees. Contact protectandserve@peirce.edu for further information.

Saban Military Wives Educational Scholarship: Through Operation Homefront and Women's Self-worth foundation.

Program is not open to spouses of active duty personnel who are pursuing a degree or certification in medical field. Two scholarships will be made available for a nursing license and twenty additional scholarships will be made available for other medical occupations.
http://operationhomefront.net/scholarship/

Surface Navy Association: Awards scholarships to members of the Surface Navy Association, their spouses, or children working toward their first undergraduate degree.
www.navysna.org

Thanks USA: Provides over 1000 scholarships for spouses of military personnel. Offers up to $5,000 each for college, vocational and technical schools. http://www.thanksusa.org

Tillman Military Scholarships: The Pat Tillman Foundation is available to currently serving members, veterans, and spouses of currently serving and veterans. Students must be pursuing an undergraduate or graduate degree as a full-time student, and must be attending a school based in the U.S. Distance learners and online programs are eligible if they are full-time programs. This is a scholarship with no specific dollar amount; the foundation considers the family's overall financial picture and awards an amount that can be used for tuition, fees, books, transportation and reasonable living expenses. For eligibility and Renewability requirements go to http://veteranaffairs.columbia.edu/content/tillman-military-scholars-scholarship

USMC Spouse Learning Series: Provides Marine Corps spouses the opportunity to further their personal and professional growth through a series of workshops and online courseware. Though targeting spouses who volunteer in their local community, the program is available to all Marine Corps spouses. Workshops and online coursework provides skills and educational development in the following areas: Relationship Building, Personal and Professional Empowerment, Business Management and Leadership, Goal

Setting, Self-care, Stress Reduction, and LifeWork Balance. http://www.usmc-mccs.org Type in: Spouse Learning Series.

USS Lake Champlain (CG-57) Scholarship Foundation: Provides assistance to spouses of members assigned to USS Lake Champlain since commissioning AUG 12, 1988. http://www.vfw.org

USS Stark Memorial Fund/Travers Loan Program/Spouse TA Program: For military spouses accompanying their husbands or wives overseas-managed by local NMCRS offices (703) 696-4960 or DSN 426-4960. www.nmcrs.org

FINANCIAL ASSISTANCE

These are a couple of emergency financial assistance organizations specifically for spouses; I have also listed financial resources under the Military Families chapter of this book as well. Plus, don't forget the many financial resources I listed in my first edition of Operation Military Resources.

Special Ops Survivors: Provide practical support including emotional and direct financial assistance to the spouses of fallen special operations service members. http://specialopssurvivors.org/

Special Ops Survivors: Provide practical support including emotional and direct financial assistance to the spouses of fallen special operations service members. http://dev.specialopssurvivors.org

ONLINE COMMUNITIES

Our service members work side by side when deployed and the lines of Guard/Reserve and active duty, rank and even branch of service tend to not matter to many. But for many spouses, they do not get the opportunity to mix as easily. Yes, many active duty families live on base but many military families don't; especially the Guard/Reserve who are spread all over the states. These families do not have the freedom or opportunity to be included in meetings, FRG's, events or expos. Because of this they miss out on many activities, updates and resources and unfortunately never even learn most resources exist. More importantly is the missed opportunity to bond, make friendships and other opportunities to connect with spouses who have "walked in their shoes." The benefits to this can be priceless and life altering.

My hope is that by adding a few of my favorite social media sites you will reach out to others and connect, share your thoughts, ideas, experiences and hopes. You will be amazed at the warm welcome you will receive and great friendships you can make.

Military Spouse Magazine: http://militaryspouse.com

Army Wife Netowrk Blog: www.armywifenetwork.com

A List of 25 different Blog Sites: http://www.circleofmoms.com/top25/military-families

AnnMarie Detevernier's "HH6 Diva" Blog: http://household6diva.com

Chris Pape's "Macho Spouse" Blog: http://machospouse.com

Reda Hicks' "Hicks Hiking Through Life" Blog:
http://hickshiking.com

Athena Hall's "Our Crazy Life" Blog:
http://mama2six.blogspot.com

Kathryn Sneed's Deployment and Military Life Blog:
http://singingthroughtherain.net

Operation Military Resources--Kimberly Suchek's Facebook page: www.facebook.com/OperationMilitaryResources

**Remember you can't just lurk or briefly show up online. For these groups to be effective for you, you need to let the group know you are there, stand in the gap between our guard/reserve and active duty communities and start healing the military-civilian divide along with finding answers, tools and resources that can be applied to your own household.*

A NETWORK OF MILITARY FAMILY-OWNED BUSINESSES ACROSS AMERICA

The Rosie Network: Is a non-profit founded by military spouses whose mission is to promote our military family-owned businesses to the public by making it easy and free to find and utilize.

What makes Rosie's Network different from other lists/sites? They are a NETWORK, not just a list and only feature military family-owned businesses. Through this network of like-minded partners, they provide access to valuable business support & resources, on-line entrepreneurial training, mentoring and more! All at **no cost** to our military members or their families, whether the business is 'just an idea' or ready to expand! Provided also is a URL-friendly **Business Profile Webpage** complete with a photo gallery, content tabs, a place for testimonials and more! This profile page is customized to suit all business needs.

All businesses within Rosie's Network are verified as military veteran or spouse-owned through ID.me (formerly TroopID) a veteran-owned company which provides verification services to the Veterans Administration, Overstock.com and many others. Your information is secure and never shared.

Eligibility to be on Rosie Network is for business owners who have served, or are married to someone who has served. Rosie proudly includes all brothers and sisters of arms including the National Guard, Coast Guard and Reserves. The Rosie Network Business Profile Webpage is a comprehensive and customizable template created to help promote ALL military family-owned businesses in our Network.

The goal being simple: to provide an online presence for our members without the cost associated with developing and hosting a website and secondly, to give online shoppers an easier format to learn about these businesses. Each Business Profile Webpage includes a contact link and content tabs for a photo gallery, description of services and more. Already have a website? We provide a link. Every webpage is given a URL-friendly web address allowing customers direct access to an individual Business Profile Webpage without the need to use the search tool. This template allows the business owner to focus on what they do best: growing their business.

So are you l**ooking for an accountant?.....a painter?...that perfect handmade gift? If so, let's assist our military community...a hire or buy from a verified military family-owned business,** http://therosienetwork.org/index.php

CHILDREN AND YOUTH

As a child, life throws many obstacles at you; many of which are the norm and part of life's growth and lessons. However a military child sees and goes through many situations that are outside of a normal growing process. Although it can be hard to be a military child, military life does make them stronger. Here are some resources to help in that endeavor.

Abidenme Books: Do you find it hard to explain military life to your children? Abidenme Books Publishing Company offers a book series that will give you the resources you need to teach your children about military lifestyle in a fun and upbeat way. The series is: Uncle Sam's Kids Series, when duty calls and Moving Again Mom by Angela Rehak. http://www.booksformilitarykids.com

Believe in Tomorrow Children Foundation: Mission is to support critically ill children of U.S. military families. http://believeintomorrow.org

Celebrate the Military Child: Is a 501(c)3 program of the SFC Jared C. Monti Memorial Scholarship Fund; that exists to bring parties to children of service members in all branches of the U.S. military and reserves to honor the sacrifice that they make. This program will bring parties to the military child. They recognize the importance of parties in the military child's life and believe that the gift of a celebration will provide normalcy, happiness and hope in these children's otherwise every changing lives. http://www.cthemc.org **Wish I would have known about them when my daughter was younger...what a cool organization.**

Childrens Institute: Of Rochester, N.Y., received funds to distribute 1,000 copies of its DVD, "Building Strong Military Families through Play," to guard and reserve centers nationwide. https://www.childrensinstitute.net/

The Comfort Crew: Supports and comforts children managing the challenges of today's military life: deployment, reintegration, moving, visible and invisible injuries, and grief. The Comfort Crew has endeavored to meet this goal by working directly with military children and families, recognizing their unique challenges, providing educational resources, and supporting physical and emotional resiliency. The Comfort Crew has also produced a series of kits to meet the specific needs of military children and hosts events designed to promote education resiliency, including our annual Camp Train 4 Life and the "With You All the Way" Symposium. http://www.comfortcrew.org **This is a favorite of mine.**

Daddy Dolls: Provides a doll with the service member's face on it. The hope is through this tool the child will still feel connected and be able to hug their parent. http://www.hugahero.com

Dads At A Distance: This provides help to fathers who spend long periods of time away from their children keep the relationship strong. http://www.daads.com

Hero's Rock: Is a non-profit that builds custom tribute rockers for the children of fallen heroes. Each rocker is created to honor each hero's line of service, has etched portraits of the hero along with their service medallions and their service title engraved in the bottom. These rockers are a comforting toy for the child at their time of loss and later an heirloom to remind them of their loved one and that our nation appreciated the great sacrifice these men and women make for their country. http://www.herosrock.us/ **These *rockers are very beautifully made and with deep respect for the families. This is one organization I am very glad came to my attention. Great Job!*

I'm Already Home: As a military "separations specialist", Elaine Dumler, aka "The Flat Daddy Lady", has been writing for military families and speaking at conferences and military installations since 2003. Her favorite thing to do is to help prepare families for deployment and the reunion/reintegration process. She has presented readiness training at installations all over the United States and has provided training materials to thousands of military families. She is the author of best sellers; I'm Already Home...Again for families experiencing deployment and The Road Home to help with reunion and reintegration. http://imalreadyhome.com/ and/or contact Elaine Dumler at Elaine@imalreadyhome.com **This is a really cool lady who shares her heart with all.**

Military Kids Connect: Your children can share their ideas and experiences with their peers in this unique, online community of military children ages 6-17. The forums are monitored. www.militarykidsconnect.org

NACCRRA: Childcare needs vary greatly among single-parent soldiers. This organization provides financial assistance for childcare that suits your unique situation. (703) 341-4100 www.NACCRRA.org

Our Military Kids: Provides grants to the children of National Guard and Military Reserve personnel who are currently deployed overseas, as well as the children of wounded warriors in ALL branches. The grants pay for participation in sports, fine arts, camps, and tutoring programs that nurture and sustain military children. These grants can pay for your children's favorite activities, such as clubs, memberships and athletic programs. www.ourmilitarykids.org (866) 691-6654 **This is probably one of my favorites for military kids. This resource was a great help for tutoring with our daughter several times.**

Random Act of Patriotism (R.A.P.): Is the newest edition of the Youth Activities Program in the Military Community. The cards and coins were created by Ambassador Lois Callahan for members to give to children who show their patriotic spirit anytime, anywhere. See a child saluting during a parade while the U.S. flag goes by? Give them a RAP card. Notice a child thanking a soldier for his or her service? Give them a RAP card. The template to print out the cards is at http://www.ladiesauxvfw.org/. And if you'd like to order the coins to go with them, call the VFW Store at (800) 821-2606.

Toys for Tots: The U.S. Marine Corps Reserve collects new, unwrapped toys during October, November, and December each year, and distributes those toys as Christmas gifts to less fortunate children in the community. www.toysfortots.com

Tutoring: This FREE confidential resource covers High School and College classes; for more information go to http://www.tutor.community/military.

United Through Reading: Provides a means for deployed service members to reach back to their children through bed time stories. United Through Reading offers deployed parents the opportunity to be video-recorded reading storybooks to their children which eases the stress of separation, maintains positive emotional connections and cultivates a love for reading. This program is available to

ALL deployed military units and at select USO locations worldwide. For more information go to www.unitedthroughreading.org/military-program.

FREE OR REDUCED COST SUMMER CAMPS

These summer camps offer a great way for our children to connect with other children from all over the world who are experiencing the same struggles, emotions and life experiences. Each camp is special in its own way and offer great coaching and different fun activities like swimming, kayaking, hiking, camping and much more. Remember your child can attend the summer camps from different states. If the cost to travel is difficult to get your child to the camp, many offer scholarships to assist.

Camp C.O.P.E.: Provides military families with an unforgettable weekend at Camp C.O.P.E while giving military kids hope, patience and courage. The camp lets them be just kids—again. Through therapeutic interventions, certified therapists teach children and their families how to cope with their changed world due to deployment, injury or loss of a family member as a result of their service to our country. Camp C.O.P.E provides weekend camps across the country FREE of charge to children and families of military personnel. http://campcope.org/

Military Teen Adventure Camp: Open to teens aged 14-18, the Military Teen Adventure Camps offer amazing summer camps with scholarships that include assistance with transportation costs. Previous year's offerings included white water rafting, extreme rock climbing, and horseback riding and much more. https://extension.purdue.edu/adventure_camps/

Children and Youth

129

Operation Purple Camp: This FREE camp for youth ages 7-17 is organized by the National Military Family Association (NMFA). In the past years, there have been locations across the country and even overseas. Offers children of deployed parents the chance to enjoy a week of summer camp for free. Along with having fun, kids gain tools that help them deal with deployments. Priority is given to children with a parent in the deployment cycle but all may apply. www.acacamps.org

Space Camp: The Military Child Education Coalition administers the Bernard Curtis Brown II Scholarships for military children to attend Space Camp in Huntsville, Alabama. This scholarship covers all costs including transportation, and is open to students in grades six through nine. http://www.militarychild.org/

Tiger Woods Learning Center: Is located in Southern California, and offers Science, Technology, Engineering and Math (STEM) camps and golf camps. Military children may receive a full scholarship for the six-day camp, but transportation costs are not covered. http://web.tigerwoodsfoundation.org/index

Golden Corral's "Camp Corral": Has an expanded summer camp program for military kids who face difficult challenges. Camp Corral provides a FREE one-week camp for kids 8-15 yrs. Parents are responsible only for the cost transportation to and from camp. This is classic summer camp: horseback riding, canoeing, swimming, fishing, target sports and a ropes course, plus campfires and nature trails. Camp Corral will be expanding nationally, providing a "week of a lifetime" to more children from more military families with a total of

nine camps nationwide. To see if one in in your state and/or to learn more about this camp go to www.campcorral.org

EDUCATION/SCHOLARSHIPS

This is one of my favorite resources for military families. The scholarships provided are humbling and much appreciated. Make sure you submitted your applications in a timely manner as many have deadlines. Remember there is NO reason your child should graduate from college in debt from student loans.

Alaska Sea Service Scholarship Fund: Applicant's Navy, Marine or Coast Guard sponsor must be a legal Alaskan resident. Applicants must be children or spouse of sponsor, who may be active duty, reserve, and retired, MIA or KIA. http://navyleague.org/scholarship/

Army Aviation Association: http://www.quad-a.org/

American Legion Scholarships: provides academic support to the children of deceased veterans who were on active duty. http://www.legion.org/scholarships
EMAIL: scholarships@legion.org

American Military Retirement Association: http://amra1973.org

American Patriot Freedom Scholarship: Is administered by Homefront America, Inc and provides 25 - $1,000 scholarships to military children who submit a winning essay. http://www.homefrontamerica.org/ click on "programs"

American Psychological Association: Scholarships and grants for under-graduate and graduate programs in the area of psychology and related disciplines. http://www.apa.org/about/awards/index.aspx

Anchor Scholarship Foundation: For dependent of active duty children or retired personnel who served in commands under the administrative control of Commanders, Naval Surface Forces, US Atlantic or Pacific Fleets for a minimum of 6 years. http://anchorscholarship.com

Armed Forces Communications and Electronics Association: Links to various grants and scholarship opportunities. http://www.afcea.org

ARTS Recognition and Talent Search Awards: Awarded to a high school or college student (17, 18 years of age) who show talent in dance, voice, music, art, photography, jazz, visual arts, writing, or other creative areas. You must audition or submit a portfolio or tape. The award is to be used for freshman year in college. Award amounts from $100 to $3,000. http://www.aie.org/scholarships

ASCO Neumatics Scholarship Program: This merit based program is for undergraduate engineering students who are in their junior or senior year and who are attending an ABET accredited engineering school. Possible internship positions are also available to students who have received the scholarship. Award is $5,000 per year. http://www.asconumatics.com

Coastline College Scholarship for Injured/Disabled Service Members & Their Spouses: Scholarship funds may be used for Coastline Classes in the next term, or subsequent terms, course materials and text books. FAX the completed form and 300 word essay to college. (714) 241-6324 http://military.coastline.edu/

Children of Fallen Patriots: This foundation provides college scholarships and educational counseling to military children who have lost a parent in the line of duty. They serve families of all branches of armed forces that have experienced combat casualties, military training accidents and other line of duty deaths. http://www.fallenpatriots.org/

Children of Fallen Soldiers Relief Fund: Provides scholarships and financial assistance to the surviving children and spouses of fallen OIF/OEF service members, and financial assistance to the families of disabled service members. (301) 685-3421 http://www.cfsrf.org/

Coast Guard Chief Warrant & Warrant Officer Association: http://www.cwoauscg.org

College Grant for Surviving Children: The Iraq/Afghanistan Service Grant is provided by the US Department of Education to children of US service members who died as a result of inquires in Iraq or Afghanistan since SEP 11, 2001. Eligible students may receive the Full Pell Grant of $5,645 for an academic year. If applicants are not eligible for the Pell Grants, they may receive an equivalent amount from the Iraq Afghanistan Service grant. Applicants may receive one or the other but not both. The Pell Grant is based on a family's financial need. Both it and the Iraq Afghanistan Service Grant are not loans and do not have to be repaid. For more information, go to http://studentaid.ed.gov/contact.

Defense Commissary Agency (DeCA): Provides scholarships for military children funded by the manufacturers and suppliers that provide support to commissaries worldwide. For more information visit www.commissaries.com and/or www.militaryscholar.org

DOLPHIN Scholarship Program: This scholarship is designed to provide financial support to dependent children of members of the US Navy Submarine community who have served at least 8 years on a submarine or 10 years on a submarine support vessel. Qualified applicants must be under the age of 24. https://www.dolphinscholarship.org

ELKS Most Valuable Student Scholarship: Designed to help high school seniors who will be attending an accredited college or university. Applicants need not be related to a member of the order in order to qualify for application. http://www.elks.org

Fallen Warrior Scholarship Fund: The Patriot Guard Riders provides scholarships to children of military service members who died in the line of duty. Students must be attending an accredited college or trade school or be a senior in high school. Contact Bill Hunt at scholarship@patriotguard.org

Fisher, Zachary and Elizabeth M. Armed Services Foundation: For children of active duty or reserve service members. https://www.fisherhouse.org/programs/scholarships-for-military-children/

Fleet Reserve Scholarship: http://www.fra.org

Folds of Honor: Provides post-secondary educational scholarships or can be applied to schooling now or held by the Foundation on behalf of young children until needed at the time of enrollment. Scholarships for children of veterans are to be used to subsidize the costs of tuition, school books, fees, room and board, special tools and equipment necessary for coursework, school-approved tutoring, and any other expense that the school in which the student is enrolled may deem appropriate and unmet. www.foldsofhonor.org

Freedom Alliance Scholarship Fund: Provides scholarships to military children of veterans who have been disabled, deceased or POW/MIA service members. www.fascholarship.com

Google/Student Veterans of America Scholarship for Computer Science: Provides scholarships valued at $10,000 and an invitation to the Google Scholars' Retreat to student veterans enrolled in computer science-related degree programs. https://www.google.com/edu/scholarships/google-sva-scholarship/#

Gold Star Scholarship Program: Is for the children and un-remarried spouses of deceased service members. http://www.nmcrs.org/pages/nmcrs-gold-star-scholarship-programs

Harry S. Truman Scholarship: This is one of the most prestigious scholarships, shaped for students who intend to pursue a career targeted to public service or government. Graduate study should be a goal, with a portion of the funds directed there. You must be at least a junior, and your college must nominate you. A "nomination package" must be created. The awards can reach as high as $30,000 over the years. Generally about 80 students are selected. http://www.truman.gov

Horatio Algers Military Scholarship: High school students who have faced & overcome great obstacles in their young lives. While many aid programs are directed primarily to recognizing academic achievement or leadership potential, the Horatio Alger program also seeks students who have a commitment to use their college degrees in service to others. http://www.horatioalger.org/scholarships/

Jason Plite College Scholarship: Each year awards scholarships to Grand Ledge, Michigan seniors in honor of their veteran son. The applicants must be involved in swimming and/or art, two of Jason's biggest interests while attending high school. http://www.jasonplitememorial.com/page2/page2.html

Marine Corps Scholarship Foundation: Is awarded to a student beginning the academic year. To be eligible, applicants must: (1) be the child of an active duty, reserve or veteran U.S. Marine who has received an honorable discharge or was killed while serving in the Corps; (2) be the child of U.S. Navy Corpsmen who is serving or have served; (3) have a GPA of at least 2.0; (4) meet an income requirement; and (5) plan to attend an accredited undergraduate college, university or vocational/technical institution in the upcoming academic year. The Scholarship Foundation gives particular attention to children whose parents has been killed or wounded in action. For more information, go to https://www.mcsf.org/

Military Child Education Coalition: Ensuring quality educational opportunities for all military children affected by mobility, family separation and transition. Programs include education programs , events, and scholarships in a wide variety of subjects such as space, literature and the arts. www.militarychild.org (254) 953-1923

Military Families Matter: Is a non-profit organization that provides cost-FREE services and support to the families of U.S. military members. Support includes providing cost-FREE birthday parties for children of deployed military members, as well as **scholarships** and unique employment assistance to military spouses and children. http://www.milfamsmatter.org

Military Scholarships: The scholarships for military children program is primarily funded through the generosity of manufacturers and suppliers whose products are sold at military commissaries, worldwide. Go to scholarships— and the right menu will provide qualifications and directions to apply. Provides college scholarship grants to children of active duty personnel, reserve/guard & retired military members or survivors of deceased members. Applicants must be enrolled, or planning to attend a full time undergraduate degree program at an accredited college or university. http://www.militaryscholar.org

Military Service Recognition Scholarship: Provides financial aid to dependents of New York military service members who were killed or permanently disabled while on active duty and who will be attending college or university in New York. http://www.veterans.ny.gov/

Sgt. Dakota Meyer Scholarship (Marines): https://www.mcsf.org

Scholarships for Military Children Program: Program is open to the children of active duty and retired customers of the commissaries. Spouses are also eligible. www.militaryscholar.org

Special Forces Charitable Trust (SFCT): The US Army Special Forces (SF) soldiers are a special breed; highly trained, fiercely proud, and quietly effective. They are the unsung heroes of the past and todays diplomatic warriors in the war on terror. In cooperation with the SFA and through active engagement with the Special Forces Command the SFCT provides programs to meet the most pressing needs of SF soldiers (past, present, future) and their families. SFCT programs include **scholarships for SF family members**; Vietnam Veteran's Assistance; job transitioning programs and family support services. http://www.specialforcescharitabletrust.org/

Special Operations Warriors Foundation Scholarship: Provides college scholarship grants based on need, along with financial aid & educational counseling to the children of Special Operations personnel who were killed in an operational mission or training accident. (813) 805-9400, www.specialops.org

Thanks USA: Spouses and children of military personnel can apply for one of nearly 1000 scholarships of up to $5,000 each for college, vocational and technical schools. Click on "scholarships" then "scholarship applications" to find lists of scholarships available and deadline dates for applications. http://www.thanksusa.org

Tillman Military Scholarships: The Pat Tillman Foundation is available to currently serving members, veterans, and their spouses of currently serving and veterans. Students must be pursuing an undergraduate or graduate degree as a full-time student, and must be attending a school based in the U.S. Distance learners and online programs are eligible if they are full-time programs. This is a scholarship with no specific dollar amount; the foundation considers the family's overall financial picture and awards an amount that can be used for tuition, fees, books, transportation and reasonable living expenses. For eligibility and renewability requirements go to http://pattillmanfoundation.org/about-us/

Tools To Assist With Education: College text books can be purchased online via electronics. Chegg offers a large selection of textbooks to either rent or buy, to learn more and save up to 85% in cost go to http://www.chegg.com/

Tutor.com for the Military: Enjoy FREE 24/7 online tutoring and homework assistance for military children grades K-12. Help is available in more than 16 subjects' http://www.tutor.com/ (800) 411-1970

USS TENNESSEE (SSBN 734) Scholarship Fund: Provides need based financial assistance in the form of a grant for the undergraduate college education of dependent children of active duty Navy personnel who are current or former members of the USS TENNESSE. http://www.nmcrs.org/spec-prgm.html

VA Mortgage Center Scholarship: Provides scholarships to active duty military personnel, honorably discharged veterans & Children of active duty military or veterans in conjunction with the Military Education Scholarship Program. www.vamortgagecenter.com/scholarships.html

**To get the most out of these scholarships, remember your extended family; the branches that your grandparents served in qualify you for those scholarships.

Also, *remember to combine these scholarships with the ones offered in the 2012 VOL I of* Operation Military Resources. *For those who wish to purchase and explore over 1,500 resources not listed in this edition go to* www.MilitaryResourceBooks.com

OUR MILITARY KIDS

Our Military Kids primary objective is to lessen the behavioral and emotional problems often experienced by children when their parents are recovering from the visible and invisible wounds of war, or while separated from a military parent serving in the National Guard or Reserve and deployed overseas.

The grants cover fees for the child's participation in an activity of their choosing that interests them in their community.

All children between the ages of 3 through 18 years of age are eligible for a grant. In addition to providing a grant of up to $500 to cover fees for 6 months of an activity, we recognize the military child's service to our country by sending a letter, certificate of appreciation, dog tags, wristband and several small trinkets.

The activities include sports and fine arts programs, tutoring, driver's training classes, 4-H projects, etc.

http://www.ourmilitarykids.org/

MILITARY FAMILY

For Volume 2, I made some changes to the layout in an attempt to make finding resource easier for you and your family; I hope this was a success. The resources provided here are for *ALL* military families...no matter the branch, era, or transition. In the event of a specific eligibility requirement I have attempted to specify/highlight this. Remember there is nothing wrong with...nor any shame in asking for help. We have all needed it at some point and many will again in the future. ALL these organization want and are honored to assist, so please reach out when you need it. If you do not find what you are looking for; feel free to email me at Kim@MilitaryResourceBooks.com I would be honored to direct you to a resource.

Adaptive Adventures Military Operations: Provides veterans fitness programs including strength conditioning, skiing, cycling, climbing, paddling, kayaking and more. http://adaptiveadventures.org/ **Looks like an awesome organization.**

Agape Foundation: Provides support, guidance and counseling services to individuals and families. http://www.agapefoundationsinc.com/

AHRN.com: One of the largest growing networks designed to improve, provide and secure available housing for relocating military members and their families. This is an awesome networking of landlords, service members, schools, community businesses and much more. www.ahrn.com ****I really have enjoyed watching this site expand over the last two years, they offer such a wide range of resources and tools needed for military families PCSing.**

Air Force Aid Society: Is helping "to relieve distress of Air Force members and their families and assisting them to finance their education" They assists in many areas of support to include financial, educational and emotional. www.afas.org

America's Fund: Provides immediate assistance and continuous support for injured heroes and their family members. www.americasfund.org ****Awesome organization.**

The American Legion: Has grouped all of the various resources and services that it offers service members and their families into its new Troop and Family Support Center at www.legion.org/family, which provides links to apply for the Legion's Family Support Network (FSN), Operation Comfort Warriors (OCW), Temporary Financial Assistance (TFA) and scholarship opportunities. The webpage also provides useful external links to helpful military resources, such as Hero Miles, which provides FREE airfare to military families, Soldiers Angels, a resource for wounded veterans and their families, and call phones for soldiers, which gives FREE calling cards to deployed service members. For more information, visit the Troop and Family Support Center.

As one of the largest veterans patriotic organizations; they are committed to mentoring youth, sponsoring wholesome programs in our communities, advocating patriotism and honor, promoting strong national security, and with continued devotion to our fellow service members and veterans. http://www.legion.org/ **One of my fan favorite organizations.**

American Music Therapy Association (AMTA): Supports organizations providing music therapy for PTSD, TBI and other emotional and cognitive issues for service members, veterans and their families. www.musictherapy.org **This organization is new to me but looks very cool.**

Army Ed Space: Provides students, parents, educators and soldiers with access to a robust directory of programs, resources and education news. Whether learning more about the variety of no cost programs available or considering the military as a future option, the site is designed to familiarize users with a host of educational programs, opportunities and effective tools to empower America's youth to make informed decisions regarding their future. www.armyedspace.com

Army Reserve Warrior Transition Liaison Program: Contains information on benefits, entitlements, financial counseling, peer support and other services for Army Reserves soldiers, veterans and their families. http://www.usar.army.mil/pages/army-reserve-warriors-transition-liaison-program.aspx

The ANC Explorer APP: On OCT 22, 2013 the Arlington National Cemetery ANC Explorer app launched for public use. This allows anyone with a smartphone or electronic tablet to visit and learn about America's most famous resting place whenever they want, from whenever they are. ANC Explorer's first version can be downloaded FREE of charge via Apple's App Store or Goggle Play. It takes 11.4 MB of space and is compatible with iPhone, iPad, iPod Touch and Android phones. The current app includes a grave site locator, digital photos of headstones, and detailed walking and driving directions. A future version will include shuttle stops; self-guided tours and event notifications.

Grave sites can be found by typing in a name, date of birth or date of death. The app can be used to plan visits to the cemetery and guide users on the grounds. They can locate monuments, memorials and notable grave sites. Anyone with a smart phone can map a route from where they are standing. This app simplifies grave research, in the past people had to go through more than 400,000 paper records to get any information. This research is now simplified. http://www.arlingtoncemetery.mil/Explore-the-Cemetery/ Find-a-Grave **Very cool app!**

Association of the U.S. Army-Family Programs: AUSA's Family Readiness Directorate is dedicated to providing Army families the assistance they need to help them manage the challenges of military life. Through four pillars of support, Education, Information, Advocacy, and Outreach, AUSA Family Readiness provides a platform from which Army families can voice their issues and concerns. **Spouse Membership Now Available:** AUSA has a new membership category for Spouses! Sign up online to have the opportunity to make your voice heard, get involved at both the national and local level, pass on wisdom to younger spouses, and get involved in issues that you care about. **RESOURCES:** Offers numerous helpful publications for military families covering topics such as deployment, parenting, reintegration and financial planning. Publications and other materials are made available to military personnel and their family members as a courtesy by AUSA's Family Readiness Directorate. www.ausa.org

Avoiding Foreclosure: VA has the tools to help – http://www. blogs.va.gov/VAntage/9801/avoiding-forclosure-va-has-the-tools-to-help/

Battling Bare: The mission is to provide a network of support for the spouses, children and family members who silently struggle to carry the burden of PTSD with their beloved service members. www.battlingbare.blogspot.com ****This is a new organization that came to my attention in 2014...I am very impressed and look forward to seeing more from them in 2015.**

Blue Star Families: Provides great support and resources. www.bluestarfam.org: This organization has developed a terrific and FREE downloadable e-book on reintegration at http://www.everyoneservesbook.com/ ****A great group of caring families.**

Caregiver Support: The VA's website dedicated to family caregivers of veterans. Caregiving can be an incredibly demanding job and the VA wants you to know you don't have to do it alone. There is a caregiver toolbox and links to find help near your home and additional resources to assist you and the families you are assisting. www.caregiver.va.gov

Center for Veterans & Their Families – The Road Home Program: Provides FREE and confidential support, counseling and veteran health services to help service members and their families understand, heal from and cope with the invisible wounds of war. http://roadhomeprogram.org

Childhelp: Helps victims of child abuse and neglect with focuses on prevention, intervention and treatment. http://www.childhelp.org/

The Coming Home Project: Coming Home Project is a non-profit organization devoted to providing expert, compassionate care, support, education, and stress management tools for Iraq and Afghanistan veterans, service members, their families, and their care providers. We are an experienced team of psychotherapists, veterans and interfaith leaders committed to alleviating the unseen wounds of war. Our nationally recognized, evidence-based programs address the emotional, social, moral, and spiritual injuries and the family challenges experienced during all stages of deployment, especially reintegration. http://www.cominghomeproject.net/ **Great organization.**

Compeer: Offers support to community based programs that serve veterans and their families, youths and the elderly with volunteer mentoring and supportive friendship programs for people with mental illnesses. http://www.compeer.org/

Corps Connections: Provides assistance, services and a network of organizations to support veterans, Navy Corpsmen, Marines and their families. Also links veterans, service members and their families with organizations that can assist with financial needs. www.corpsconnections.org.

Department of Housing & Urban Development (HUD) – Housing Vouchers: Under the HUD-VASH programs, combines Housing Choice Voucher rental assistance for homeless veterans with case management and clinical services provided by the VA. For more information, call the National Call Center for Homeless Veterans at 877-4AID-VET.

Disabled Sports USA: Offers sports rehabilitation programs, including winter skiing, aquatic sports, competition and special sports events, to anyone with a permanent disability. The Warfighter Sports Program serves wounded warriors, including those injured in the Iraq and Afghanistan wars, through sports rehabilitation programs in military hospitals and communities across the U.S. Also has a great Youth program. www.disabledsportsusa.org

DSTRESS Line: Developed by the Marine Corps to provide professional, anonymous counseling for Marines, attached Sailors and families when it's needed most. www.dstressline.com

Familyofavet.com: http://www.familyofavet.com

The Fisher House Foundation: Provides a "home away from home" for military families to be close to a loved one during hospitalization for an illness, disease or injury. https://www.fisherhouse.org ****Great organization.**

Full Circle Home: Arranges for gift boxes to be sent on behalf of deployed service members to family members at home during the holidays. The boxes contain a variety of pampering products and a hand written note to help comfort and support military spouses and mothers during separation. http://www.fullcirclehome.org/ ****This is a new resource that came to my attention in 2014...I definitely can see the benefits for many military families to utilizing this resource.**

Gold Star Mothers Program: Provides financial support to the American Gold Star Mothers (AGSM) Inc. This is an organization of mothers whose children have died while in military service, died as a result of that service or are missing in action. The non-profits objectives are to assist veterans, active duty military and their families. This is accomplished by the veterans Administration Volunteer Services activities in veteran hospitals, centers and cemeteries. Their members provide venues of learning and fellowship and provide resources on grief support and information on national and state legislative issues. The American Gold Star Mothers members assist many community organizations with the assistance of veterans of Foreign Wars (VFW) and its Ladies Auxiliaries. http://www.goldstarmoms.com/ ****Great group of caring families.**

Guardian Angels for Soldiers Pet: Supports are active duty military, wounded warriors, homeless veterans and their beloved pets to ensure the pets are reunited with their owners following a deployment related to a combat or peace-keeping or humanitarian mission or unforeseen medical and/or homeless hardship situation through various programs/services/projects. www.guardianangelsforsoldierspet.org ****Love this group, they are a fan favorite.**

GOVBenefits.gov: Helps citizens access government benefits eligibility information through a FREE confidential, and easy-to-use online screening tool. After answering some basic questions, the user receives a customized report listing the benefit programs for which the user, or person for whom he/she is entering information. www.GOVBenefits.gov/

Healing Horses & Armed Forces: Supports veterans and their families through Equine Assisted Psychotherapy (EAP) therapies designed to address symptoms of post-disorder (PTSD) and military sexual trauma (MST); offers spouse and family programs. http://www.risingmoonranch.org ****New to my attention but this is already a favorite, I firmly believe this type of therapy is helpful and needed for ALL of us.**

HeartsApart.org: Was created to keep families connected while our military men and women are serving abroad. Through the efforts of our community's finest photographers, HeartsApart.org provides our soon to be deployed servicemen and women with pictures of their spouses and children. The photographs are printed on waterproof and durable bi-folded cards, which fit securely in their uniform pocket. HeartsApart.org believes that our military personnel deserve and need the memory of their families to carry them through the difficult times that lie ahead. www.HeartsApart.org ****What a wonderful and caring idea..love it.**

Heroes At Home, LLC: Was created to help deployed military personnel celebrate, honor and stay in touch with their heroes at home. Heroes At Home believe military families are made up of two types of heroes: those who risk their lives to defend our country and those who keep households and families together while their loved ones are deployed. Services provided our: deployment coaching, gift services, military family database, deployment newsletter, blogs and forum, speaking services and a book. http://www.myheroesathome.com/blog/description/ ****Just learned about them and I enjoy this site.**

Homes for All Veterans: Manages services to promote housing stability and alleviate chronic homelessness. Funded through a grant from the VA. http://rmhumanservices.org/program/homes-all-veterans.

Horizon Outreach: Provide supportive services, resources and housing to military and non-military families facing challenging life situations. http://www.horizonoutreach.org

Iraq & Afghanistan Veterans of America (IAVA): Provides a wide range of assistance for our military families. EMAIL: info@IAVA.org www.IAVA.org ****FAN FAVORITE.**

Jewish War Veterans: http://www.jwv.org/

Legal Aid Society of Columbus: Supplies pro bono legal aid to veterans, service members and their families including VA and state benefits, discharge status upgrades, homeless/at-risk assistance, and other civil legal issues. http://www.columbuslegalaid.org

Library of Congress – Veterans History Project (VHP): Collects, preserves and makes accessible the personal accounts of American war veterans. Use the database search to browse the VHP collection. For more information

Military Family

visit http://www.loc.gov/vets/ Also **StoryCorps – Military Voice Initiative** records, preserves and shares the stories of veterans, service members and military families. http://storycorps.org/military-voices/ ****I will take a closer look at this as I find it to be very cool and interesting.**

Lifestyle Insights, Networking, Knowledge and Skills (L.I.N.K.S.) (USMC): Mission is to act in an advisory capacity to the Family Readiness Committee (FRC) of the Marine Corps Community Services Board of Directors on all matters that impact the LINKS Program. The subcommittee functions as a broker and clearinghouse for all LINKS issues and concerns and will ensure regular communication with the field through major commands and installations. This website also provides numerous other resources for spouses and families. http://www.usmc-mccs.org/

Marines & Mickey: Marines and Mickey has two missions. The first is to send Marines who have recently returned from an overseas Deployment, Recruiting Duty or the Drill Field to Disney with their families. The second is to assist families who cannot afford to attend their new Marines Boot Camp Graduation due to financial hardships. www.marinesandmickey.org ****AWESOME!!**

Marine Parents: Offers links to various sites, resources and tools needed for our community. For example, "What's after Boot" is a community for parents, spouses, and family members of newly graduated Marines. This program of MarineParents.com will help answer some of the questions you and/or your new Marine may have about what to expect after boot camp. http://www.marineparents.com/marinecorps/ ****Great useful information.**

Mid-Atlantic Bulldog Rescue: Is run by a military family and assists military families in adopting pets. Volunteers provide a safe and loving home for bulldogs in transition. www.midatlanticbulldogrescue.com ****FAN FAVORITE.**

Military Money: Provides online information and planning tools for military service members and their families about money management, education and career advice, deployment and relocation; created as part of US Department of Defenses "Financial Readiness Campaign." https://www.incharge.org/military-money

Military Families Learning Network: Provides support to service members and their families through engaged online communities providing best practices, information, educational and curriculum materials, and programming activities and efforts. http://blogs.extension.org/militaryfamilies/ **Useful information.**

Military Home Front: Special Needs/Exceptional Family Member Connections Program: Is now on the Military Home Front website under Troops and Families: Special Needs. This program provides information on services and resources available to military families with special medical or educational needs. More specifically the website features resources and information on financial issues, legal issues, medical care, education and family support. Members of the network can also contact other military families with special needs to share solutions to common problems. http://www.dodlive.mil/ **Very useful information.**

Military Families Matter: Is a non-profit organization that provides cost-free services and support to the families of U.S. military members. Support includes providing cost-free birthday parties for children of deployed military members, as well as scholarships and unique employment assistance to military spouses and children. http://www.milfamsmatter.org

The Military Family Network: Find, support and improve your well-being through connections with organizations in your community that provide excellent service for military families. www.eMilitary.org (412) 531-1970 **Great site-- fan favorite.**

Military Town Advisor: Is a site dedicated to assisting service members and their families with PCSing to safe, family friendly and in areas where other military families live if desired. MilitaryTownAdvisor.com provides the "insider" information about the neighborhoods and areas of the town by bases of assignments. Soon this site will be adding GreatSchools data and Home Search functions so viewer can search homes within a specific neighborhood or zip code. This is a research tool to help military families understand where the safe neighborhoods are in a new military town. www.MilitaryTownAdvisor.com

Military Outreach USA: Serves service members, veterans, and their families by connecting them to network of individuals and faith-based resources in their local community. http://www.militaryoutreachusa.org

MilitaryOneSource: A DoD sponsored website which contains numerous resources for military spouse and families. Requires setting up an account to access the military branch pages. (800) 342-9647 is available 24 hours a day/ http://www.militaryonesource.com **Fan favorite.**

Military Ovation: Supports veterans and their families through employment, education, training and support programs. www.nd.gov

Military Warriors Support Foundation – Homes4WoundedHeroes: Awards Mortgage-FREE homes to wounded service members injured during combat in Iraq and Afghanistan. In addition to the home, the families will receive three years of family and financial mentoring. www.militarywarriors.org **Fan favorite.**

Military Warriors Support Foundation – Homes4GoldStars: Awards mortgage-free homes to survivors. http://militarywarriors.org/programs/ **Fan favorite.**

Military Warriors Support Foundation – Skills4Life: Provide family mentoring and recreational outings such as hunting, fishing, golf, sporting events, family outings, vacations and 100% mortgage free homes to Gold Star spouses. www.militarywarriors.org **Fan favorite.**

My Military Mommy: My Military Mommy lists where the best discounts are for military families. http://www.mymilitarymommy.com/

NACCRRA: Childcare needs vary greatly among single-parent soldiers. This organization provides financial assistance for childcare that suits your unique situation. www.NACCRRA.org (703) 341-4100 **Very useful and provide a great service to our community.**

National Association of Black Veterans: http://www.nabvets.org

National Guard Professional Education Center – Guard Support Center (GSC): Provides Army National Guard soldiers and their families information and counseling on education benefits and resources, civilian employment assistance and one-on-one coaching. http://www.pec.ng.mil/

National Guard Family Program: This organization facilitates communication between Guard families and the Guard, and provides FREE financial, household, emotional and health support services. The program operates on a state-by-state basis. www.jointservicessupport.org/FP/Default.aspx.

National Military Family Association – Legal Benefits: Find where to go for legal support for such things as Power of

Attorney, Wills, Advance Directives, Living Wills and other legal affairs.
http://www.militaryfamily.org/your-benfits/legal/

National Veterans Foundation: Offers veterans and their families crisis and information services through the nation's first toll-free, vet-to-vet hotline for all U.S. veterans and their families in addition their veteran counselors provide veterans and their families with information, counseling and service referrals for issues around VA benefits, mental health counseling, housing, medical services, education benefits, financial issues and more. www.nvf.org

Navy-Marine Corps Relief Society (NMCRS): provides financial, educational and other assistance to members of the Naval Services and their family members and survivors. www.nmcrs.org

Navy Knowledge On-line: Offical Navy website for sailor career management, personal development, leadership development, E-Learning, and other reverence materials. This website is available to authorized family members. It also provides specific information for individual Augmentees (IA). E-Learning courses include numerous subjects including Microsoft Office Software. https://wwwa.nko.navy.mil

The National Resource Society for Women Veterans: http://www.rfwv.org/

Online College Database: Search in this directory of online colleges and universities for information on tuition, enrollment, university type and ranking. http://www.onlinecollegesdatabase.org

Operation Care and Comfort (OCC): Americans support our troops serving in times of war in many ways: Writing letters, mailing care packages, welcome home events, or

by showing support for a deployed service member or veteran's family. The unique programs of OCC carries on this tradition allowing caring Americans to donate their time, talent, and treasure to honor those currently serving our country and those who have served.
https://www.occ-usa.org/

Operation Family Caregiver: Customizes a 16 to 26 week program that is unique to the families of those who have served. http://www.operationfamilycaregiver.org/

Operation Homefront: Provides emergency financial and other assistance to service members, wounded warriors and their families. OH provides direct services to alleviate a military family's or individual's actual/complete emergency financial burden, as well as counseling and/or recovery support. www.operationhomefront.net (click on your state, if one not located by you-go to national for assistance). ****Fan favorite.**

Operation Homefront – Homes on the Homefront: Awards mortgage – free homes to veterans. In addition to the home, the families will build a customized transition plan with program staff. http://www.homesonthehomefront.org/ ****Fan favorite.**

Operation Military Family: This site offers a comprehensive support/resource network and action plan website for our military community. http://militarymomsmm.com ****Fan favorite.**

Operation Paperback: Receives and distributes reading materials to overseas locations, USO centers, and military and VA hospitals through a volunteer shipping network. http://www.operationpaperback.org/

Operation Shoebox: Sends care packages to service members overseas and wounded warriors.
http://operationshoebox.com

Operation VetHaven: Assigns a personal advocate to service member, veterans and their families with post-traumatic stress disorder (PTSD) and traumatic brain injury (TBI).
http://operationvetshaven.org **Great idea and resource.**

Operation We Are Here: Is a resource HUB for the military community and military supporters. We offer a clearinghouse of resources for the military community, practical insights in caring for the military community, the ONLY interest-based list for military supporters, and much more. The mission of Operation We Are Here is: to create an awareness of the challenges of the military community, to offer practical suggestions to churches, community and individuals on how to support and encourage the military community, to provide a comprehensive list of resources for the military community and its supporters.
www.operationwearehere.com ***This is a great website, with a great team for support.***

Patriot Guard Riders: Attends memorial and funeral services for service members to honor and shield the family from interruptions created by protestors.
www.patriotguard.org **HUGE fan...love this group and their generosity is humbling. They travel ALL over the U.S. on their own time to provide comfort, respect and peace of mind. Can't say enough good things about this group.**

Powerful Tools for Caregivers: This organization has some excellent tools for caregivers. While it may seem geared toward the aging, the materials available offer excellent insight into self-care. Use the contact button to ask questions about materials that could be targeted to the special needs of your situation.
https://www.powerfultoolsforcaregivers.org/

Professional Tutors of America – Military and Veterans Program: Offers academic services nationwide to wounded warriors, service members, veterans and their families including customized, one-on-one tutoring and career coaching. http://www.professionaltutors.com/military **Fan favorite.**

Project Evergreen: Preserving and enhancing green space in our communities for today and future generations. GreenCare for troops is a nationwide outreach program coordinated by Project Evergreen that connects local green industry professionals with men and women serving our country in the armed forces away from home. GreenCare for Troops is in the process of helping hundreds of volunteers provide FREE lawn care and landscape services (snowplowing too) for thousands of military families nationwide. http://projectevergreen.org/ **Fan favorite. They helped me with snowplowing when my husband was deployed and I was very gratefull.**

The Real Warriors Campaign: Engage in the community, learn about religious and military services, developed relationships with other Guard family members, and gain tools for navigating the deployment process. www.realwarriors.net (866) 966-1020

REBOOT Workshops - National Veterans Transition Services: Teaches veterans how to make social, civilian and career transitions. http://www.nvtsi.org.

Salvation Army Liberty Program: Provides emergency assistance for OIF/OEF veterans and their families in areas of: childcare/preschool, grocery/food voucher, rental assistance, clothing vouchers, calling cards, gas vouchers, utilities, college books, case management and counseling. www.veteranstoday.com

SEAL Legacy Foundation: Supports families of wounded and fallen Navy Seals, educational assistance for SEALs and their families and other charitable causes benefitting the SEAL community. https://www.seallegacy.org/

Semper FI Fund: Provides immediate financial support for injured and critically ill members of the U.S. Armed Forces and their families. https://SemperFiFund.org

Soldiers' Angels: Provides assistance for active duty military persons and families in areas of blankets, care packages, holiday gifts to deployed soldiers and emergency travel assistance. www.soldiersangels.org

The Soldiers Project: The Soldiers Project provides **free** counseling to service members of all branches of the military, regardless of discharge status, as well as their loved ones. Their services are free, confidential and unlimited.

They have a network of more than 450 licensed, mental health professionals, community outreach, and educational workshops for our therapists in military culture, PTSD and other psychological effects of war; The Soldiers Project has been able to help ease the transition back to civilian life for veterans and their families.

The Soldiers Project clients come from all branches of the military and include pre-deployed, active duty, veterans, National Guard and Reserve service members, as well as spouses, parents, and children.

First step is to contact them via telephone or email and answer a few questions. Their Intake Coordinators will then find a therapist that meets your needs in terms of location, session times and other factors essential to providing customized care. All services are free of charge, and their therapists have all agreed to help our community for as long as needed. You can request individual or couples counseling or even family therapy. https://www.thesoldiersproject.org/

For more information please fill out the form on the website or call (877) 576-5343.

Special Forces Charitable Trust (SFCT): The US Army Special Forces (SF) soldiers are a special breed; highly trained, fiercely proud, and quietly effective. They are the unsung heroes of the past and todays diplomatic warriors in the war on terror. In cooperation with the SFA and through active engagement with the Special Forces Command the SFCT provides programs to meet the most pressing needs of SF soldiers (past, present, future) and their families. SFCT programs include scholarships for SF family members; Vietnam Veteran's Assistance; job transitioning programs and family support services. Questions can be directed to Mr. David Guernsey, Executive Director at (860) 767-1510 http://www.specialforcescharitabletrust.org/

Spirit of Sharing: This non-profit organization provides the elements of the holiday season that a family might not ordinarily be able to enjoy. S.O.S strives to build a relationship with each family to gain better insight and understanding of individual and familial needs and interests. Each family is generally provided with several weeks' worth of groceries and all of the goodies that make the holiday season so warm, comforting, and special. S.O.S. also provides each child in these families with age appropriate and personal gifts including clothing, educational materials and toys. http://www.spiritofsharing.org

Still Serving Veterans: Are passionate about helping Veterans and their families receive all the benefits and services they have earned, connecting them to other vital veteran support resources within their community, and significantly expanding their career opportunities. They accomplish these goals through empowerment and expert, caring case management; education assistance and training; and by engaging the community to serve alongside their team and veterans. http://www.stillservingveterans.org/

Support the Enlisted Project (STEP): Provides emergency financial and transition assistance grants to active duty and recently discharge enlisted military and their families. http://www.stepsocal.org

Financial Freedom Seminars: Presents FREE financial planning seminars to teach military and veteran families money-saving strategies and techniques to help them get out of debt and reach their financial goals. https://embassyinstitute.org/financial

Tips & Guidebooks for Families : Provides assistance to military families in areas of PTSD. www.militaryvetswithPTSD.com

United Service Organization (USO): Provides support services, recreation activities and volunteer opportunities for service members and military families. http://www.uso.org/ **Fan favorite.

US Troop Support Foundation: Provide care packages and assistance to all military personnel in need, providing funds are available and the need is legitimate. US Troop Support Foundation will assist Military families in need with any assistance within reason and means, with board majority approval. No direct cash funding will be done. http://www.ustroopsupport.com/

US Vet Source: Provide workshops and support services to veterans and their families that are returning to civilian life or dealing with challenges. https://www.usvetsource.org/

VETRN.org: Is an Entrepreneurship Training and Resource Network for Veterans; they provide vets & family an app of FREE tuition to attend a program in entrepreneurship at NE University School of Business and provide them with the skills, resources, networking and mentorship necessary to launch or grow a small business. This program is being presented in partnership with NE University D'Amore-McKim School of Business and Center of Entrepreneurship. http://www.vetrn.org/

Vet Commander: A new, veteran created and operated mobile and web platform that provides veterans face-time with their dream employer at the click of a button, delivering 60 second pre-recorded video interviews, a mobile app, and a nationwide events program that connects veterans to employers and military veteran advocates. https://www.vetcommander.com/

Vets Group: A D.C. non-profit based organization providing economic empowerment support for veterans/their families through education, entrepreneurship, and mentoring and employment opportunities. http://vetsgroup.org ****Very cool.**

Veteran Consortium Pro Bono Program: Pro Bono legal aid for veterans and their family members who have an appeal pending at the US Court of Appeals for veterans Claims ONLY. (888) 838-7727.

Veteran Guide to Mesothelioma, Asbestos Exposure & Lung Cancer: Presents a guide to help veterans, families of veterans and veterans organizations understand mesothelioma from asbestos exposure. http://www.cooneyconway.com/

Veteran Oral History Projects: Use this list from the Library of Congress to find repositories collecting and persevering oral histories, memoirs and other materials related to veterans and wartime experiences. http://www.loc.gov/vets/relatedrepositories.html

Veteran to Technicians: Audi of America, Inc., has established the veterans to Technicians Program to meet the growing and predicted future dealership demand for talented and experienced technicians. The purpose of the veterans to Technicians Program is to attract skilled former military maintenance technicians to become brand-certified Audi Serve Technicians, Shop Foreman and Service Consultants, which will expand the pool of qualified personnel employed by authorized Audi dealership.

Audi of America is pleased to announce this opportunity to welcome skilled veterans into their organization and culture through the veterans to Technicians Program, one of several exciting initiatives designed to expand the quality, diversity and depth of the Audi Service Technician, Shop Forman and Service Consultant workforce. http://www.audivets.com

Veteran Tickets Foundation (Vet Tix): Provides FREE event tickets to our military, veterans and their families, also to family members of troops Killed In Action (K.I.A.). The events include sporting events, concerts, performing arts and family activities. http://www.vettix.org ****Fan favorite.**

Vietnam Veterans of America: A great resource full of valueable support and resources for our veterans and their families. http://www.vva.org

Vietnam Veteran Wives: Offers counseling and assistance with VA filings, Chapter 35 benefit filings and burial benefits. www.vietnamveteranwives.org

Victory Village: Victory Village Amador-Amador county veterans organization: Their mission is to serve those who have served our great nation by facilitating veteran services for our service members, veterans and their families. They accomplish this by a streamline access to veterans housing, employment, healthcare and training. In support of our Military and families they are bridging the gap from military service to civilian life. www.victoryvillagevets.org/

Volunteers of America Chesapeake: Takes great pride in doing everything possible for our nation's veterans. While their sacrifices are too often forgotten when they return home, this short sightedness inspires them to do even more to ease veterans transitions and help them find purpose in civilian life. http://www.voachesapeake.org/

W.O.M.E.N: Women's Online Media & Education Network http://www.womencorp.com ****Fan favorite.**

Yellow Ribbon Reintegration Program – EventPLUS: Enables community partners, vendors, staff, Reserve Component Services Members and their families to find and register for upcoming Yellow Ribbon Events. **Yellow Ribbon Reintegration Program – Agenda Builder:** Offers Yellow Ribbon Reintegration Programs (YRRP) event planners and staff a simple interface to build, edit, and publish agendas. www.militaryonesource.mil

EDUCATIONAL/SCHOLARSHIPS

It is no secret this is one of my favorite resources for our military community. Education is so important but requires one of the most expensive investments in order to accomplish. The sacrifice made not only by your spouse, parent, grandparents etc...is honored with these scholarships. Please keep their memories and sacrifices alive by taking the time to apply. Why graduate in debt when their service can live on through you? Please share these as most military families do not know they exists.

AFCEA – Armed Forces Communications & Electronic Assoc. Education Foundation: Offers a large variety of scholarship programs for both active duty personnel and their families.

These scholarships are based on the field of study, primarily in intelligence studies; cyber security, mathematics; science, and engineering scholarships are available for undergraduate and graduate programs, and disabled veterans. (This can be used by service members who are still on active duty or in conjunction with their veterans benefits).
http://www.afcea.org/education/scholarships/info.asp

Air Force Aid Society Education Grant (General Henry H. Arnold Education Grants Program): This is a merit-based program that is open to dependent children of active duty members, Title 10 AGR Reservists & Deceased personnel, as well as the surviving spouses of deceased personnel.
http://www.afas.org/education-grants

Ambassadorial Scholarships: This is the prestigious "Rotary" organization scholarship for students who can speak another language and want to study abroad in the "host" country of that language. Award amounts are from $10,000 to $23,000 for a 3 month to full year of study abroad. You should have completed at least 2 years of college work. For additional information on this program you can call (866) 976-8279.
http://en.wikipedia.org/wiki/Ambassadorial_Scholarships

American Society of Naval Engineers: This program seeks to encourage students to pursue a degree in the field of naval engineering and related disciplines. This will fund the senior year of college or the first year of a graduate program.
www.navalengineers.org

Bowfin Memorial Scholarship: For members of the Hawaii submarine force personnel (active or retired), their family members and family members of deceased submariners. Applicants and sponsors must live and attend college in Hawaii. EMAIL: dcpcc@aol.com (808) 455-2597

Coast Guard Mutual Assistance: For scholarship information http://www.cgmahq.org/ (800) 881-2462

Council of College and Military Educators: This program is designed to help support active duty military personnel and their families to help with the expense of going to college. http://www.ccmeonline.org

Joseph A. McAlinden Divers Scholarship: Offers specifically to Navy and Marine Corps Divers, whether active duty or retired and their eligible family members. This scholarship provides financial assistance for full-time undergraduate and graduate students, who must be participating in one of the following areas of study: oceanography, Ocean Agriculture, or Aquaculture. There is no deadline for this program. http://www.nmcrs.org/pages/joseph-a.-mcalinden-divers-scholarship-program

Eknowledge: FREE SAT & ACT prep kits available. Children and relatives of National Guard can get these kits compliments of professional athletes and testing company eKnowledge. The SAT and ACT PowerPrep Program, which retails for $200+ is available FREE upon request (there is a nominal charge of $17.55 per program for materials and shipping). The DVD consists of 11 hours of video instruction, 3,000 files of supplemental test prep materials, sample questions and practice tests. www.eKnowledge.com/USNG

Embarg Scholarship: Administered by the Low Country Chapter of the Military Officer's Association of America. c/o Harold Hirshman, 137 Chowan Creek Bluff, Beaufort, SC 29907.

Federal Student Aid Scholarship Search: Offers a scholarship search, financial aid and scholarship wizard. https://studentaid.ed.gov/sa/

Fleet Reserve Association (FRA) (for dependents of members only): Members can be active duty, reserve retired personnel of Navy, Marine Corps, or the Coast Guard. http://www.fra.org

Free Application for Federal Student Aid: Federal Student Aid, an office of the U.S. Department of Education, ensures that all eligible individuals can benefit from federally funded or federally guaranteed financial assistance for education beyond high school. www.fafsa.ed.gov

Folds of Honor: This pair of scholarships is for spouses and children of deceased, 100% disabled, POW/MIA and Purple Heart Recipients. Scholarships are awarded for both immediate use programs and future-used scholarships for school-age children which are held in trust until needed. http://www.foldsofhonor.com/scholarships

GovBenefits.gov: Provides useful educational benefits tools. http://www.benefits.gov/

Hispanic Scholarship Fund: Offers several scholarship programs for students of Hispanic heritage. http://hsf.net

Ladies Auxiliary of the First Fleet Reserve Auxiliary Scholarship: Provides academic support to members of the Navy, Marine Corps and the Coast Guard and their families. http://www.la-fra.org.

Military.com: This commercial site has information on scholarship opportunities for military family member. Visit the site to find grant money for school. www.military.com

Military Community Scholarship and Financial Aid Explorer: Provides military members and their families' research scholarship and financial aid opportunities. www.mcsfex.net

Military Family Scholarships: National Military Family Association offers scholarships for spouses and children of active duty personnel. http://www.militaryfamily.org

Military Officers Association: Provides multiple scholarship opportunities for our military community. Visit their website for details at http://www.moaa.org/

Military Order of the Purple Heart Scholarship: For recipients of the Purple Heart, their spouses and dependents children. Amount is determined by need and type of degree. Dependents of deceased Purple Heart recipients are also eligible for this scholarship. http://www.purpleheart.org/scholarships

Military Warriors Support Foundation: Scholarship awards will be for those leaving the military because of their wounds or for family members of those lost in Iraq or Afghanistan. MWSF also provides coaching and mentoring programs to veterans who are attending college on these scholarships. http://militarywarriors.org/education4heroes

National Military Family Association NMFA): Offers detailed information about education, choosing scholarships, grants, financial aid, and resources for foreign-born spouses. http://www.militaryfamily.org

Navy League of San Diego: Need based scholarships for Navy & Marine Corps dependents who reside in California and are a graduating senior who has been accepted to an accredited college or university. www.navyleague-sd.com

The Navy-Marine Corps Relief Society: Provides need based financial assistance for full-time undergraduate students. For: Children of active-duty Sailors and Marines (including Reservists while on active duty over 90 days), children of

retired sailors and marines and spouses of active duty sailors and marines residing within the 50 states.
http://www.nmcrs.org/

Officers' Wives' Club: Camp Pendleton Officers Wives Club has a wide-variety of scholarships available for military spouses and dependent children.
http://www.aowcgwa.org/

Officers Spouses' Club of San Diego, Inc. Scholarship: To dependent children and spouses of active duty, retired, or deceased military officers and enlisted personal. Applicants must reside in the greater San Diego area at time of application. Applicants contact the Wives Club of America Scholarship Foundation.
http://www.noscsandiego.com/scholarships

OnlineSchool.org: A new and expanding project (2013) that allows users to search and locate all non-profit higher education intuition with online course offerings. This is a viable economical higher educational solution for individuals of all ages. Through the projects robust search function, they have created an experience that allows individuals to search and locate the nonprofit online college solution best suited to them. A resource that is 100% FREE. http://onlineschool.org

The Post G.I. Bill: Is the official website of the U.S. government with information on over a thousand benefit and assistance programs. They include education grants and loans, health, housing, and other types of assistance. To obtain a tailored list of benefit programs for which you may be eligible, complete the free and confidential questionnaire on the GovBenefits.gov homepage. http://www.gibill.va.gov

Scholarships for Severely Injured Service Members and their Dependents: www.usveteransmagazine.com

Students.gov: This U.S. Department of Education site links students with information on financial aid, tuition assistance, and scholarships. There is a section for military members and their families. Start your search by going to "Pay for your education." www.students.gov

Surface Navy Association: Awards scholarships to members of the Surface Navy Association, their spouses, or children working toward their first undergraduate degree. http://navysna.org.

Thanks USA Scholarship Program: Provides scholarships to active duty personnel, veterans AND their family members. (877) 849-8727 or (507) 931-0408. https://www.scholarshipamerica.org/thanksusa/

Tutor.com for the Military: Enjoy FREE, 24/7 online tutoring and homework assistance for military children grades K-12. Help is available in more than 16 subjects. www.tutor.com/military (800) 411-1970.

USA Learning: Is the official learning and development site for the US Federal Government. USALearning supports the development of the federal workforce and advances the accomplishment of agency missions through simplified and one-stop access to high quality e-learning products. www.GoLearn.gov

USA4 Military Families: Is a state partnership initiative that seeks to engage and educate state policymakers, not-for-profit associations, concerned business interests, and other state leaders about the needs of military members and their families, particularly as those needs intersect with state public policy. Through state/military partnership, DoD seeks to develop relationships with states, work with them to remove unnecessary barriers, and significantly improve the quality of life for military families.www.USA4MilitaryFamilies.dod.mil

USMC Spouse Learning Series: Provides Marine Corps Spouses the opportunity to further their personal and professional growth through a series of workshops and online courseware. Though targeting spouses who volunteer in their local community, the program is available to all Marine Corps spouses. The traid of workshops and online courseware provides skills and educational development in the following areas: Relationship Building, Personal and Professional Empowerment, Business Management and Leadership, Goal Setting, Self-ccare, Stress Reduction, and LifeWork Balance. http://www.usmc-mccs.org Type in: Spouse Learning Series.

Wings Over America: Provide college scholarships to dependent children and spouses of all US Navy personnel—officer and enlisted—active duty, retired, honorably discharged, or deceased who served within Naval Air Forces. http://www.wingsoveramerica.us/

**Make sure you utilize ALL the resources in the best way possible. For example….Yes, you may have the G.I Bill available for your dependents to use towards their education but why use it straight away when these scholarships can pay for the Associate Degree…especially when you live at home or attend a Community College. Save the GI Bill for when your dependents are working on their BA Degree or move to an out of state college or university. By that time they will definitely need the living stipend that will provide them the means to focus on studying (instead of working to pay bills), internships and volunteer work which will look great on their resumes.

FINANCIAL

Can't find financial resource to fit your needs with the ones listed? Make sure to review the resources offered in Operation Military Resources Volume 1 offered at www.MilitaryResourceBooks.com and online wherever books are sold.

Air Force Aid Society: Is helping "to relieve distress of Air Force members and their families and assisting them to finance their education" They assists in many areas of support to include financial, educational and emotional. www.afas.org

Army Emergency Relief: AER is the Army's own emergency financial assistance organization and is dedicated to "Helping the Army Take Care of its Own." *Provides assistance in areas of: **Family Dental Care Assistance** now covers diagnosis, fillings, crowns, root canals, extractions, sealants and emergency care. Assistance is limited to no more than $4,000. * **Basic Furniture Needs:** For Army families who move into quarters with no furniture or for those who low their furniture in natural disasters will be capped at $4,000. * **Assistance**: not to exceed $4,000 – is available for soldiers for soldiers to replace their current vehicle when the cost to repair it is more than it's worth. **Rental Vehicle Assistance** is available for soldiers on emergency leave or waiting for the repair of their primary vehicle. The rental period would normally be seven to 10 days. **The Army Spouse Scholarship** program has been consolidated. Now, spouses - both overseas and stateside – will only have to apply once a year for scholarship programs and be eligible for assistance while attending school part-time. AER provides commanders a valuable asset in accomplishing their basic command responsibility for the morale and welfare of soldiers. www.aerhq.org

Armed Forces Relief Trust: Links to the Air Force Aid Society, Army Emergency Relief, Coast Guard Mutual Assistance, and

Navy-Marine Corps Relief Society, which provide emergency assistance to service members and their families; eligibility and qualifying expenses, vary for each relief fund. http://www.afrtrust.org

Bob Woodruff Foundation: Provides assistance in several areas; one being emergency financial assistance for wounded warriors and their families. www.bobwoodrufffoundation.org

Coast Guard Assistance Fund: Imagine your loved one graduating from Bootcamp with no one there to celebrate with them. Our fund helps family members attend the graduation of their recruit from Coast Guard bootcamp when they could not otherwise afford to attend. 100% of your donations will help a mother, father, grandparent, spouse or sibling attend when no one else will be there. Their goal is for every recruit to be represented at graduation. This fund is a 501©3 non-profit organization and all donations are tax deductible. The fund is run by volunteers who have children in the Coast Guard. http://www.cgfaf.org/

Coast Guard Mutual Assistance (CGMA): CGMA provides essential financial aid to the entire Coast Guard Family, primarily through interest-FREE loans, grants, and financial counseling.

Established and operated by Coast Guard people for Coast Guard people, CGMA provides a way to extend compassion to one another in times of need. It serves as a vital financial safety net, promoting financial stability and general well-being, fostering high morale and encouraging a sense of loyalty to the Coast Guard. www.cgmahq.org

Military OneSource: Get sound financial counseling with a professional consultant in your community, in person or by phone. www.MilitaryOneSource.mil (800) 342-9647

Navy Marine Corps Relief Society (NMCRS): Provides financial assistance and education, as well as other programs and services to members of the United States Navy and Marine Corps, their family members, widows and survivors. The society also receives and manages donated funds to administer these programs and services. The Society's main goal is to help each person who comes to us get support for their immediate needs. Our long-term mission is to help Sailors and Marines become financially self-sufficient by learning how to better manage their personal finances and prepare for unplanned expenses. www.nmcrs.org

Operation Family Fund: Provides financial grants for each eligible member or members family to meet personal, short and long term living needs in these areas; food, rent, utilities, emergency transportation and vehicle repair, funeral expenses, legal expenses, medical/dental expenses, assistance with home, rental, lease, purchase or home improvements, assistance with the purchase, rent or lease of a vehicle. The Board of Directors has final approval of all funds allocation and selection of money managers. www.operationfamilyfund.org ****Fan favorite.**

Operation First Response: For many veterans and families the financial hardship begins quickly and for others it is after the domino effect of extra costs and lost wages. At whatever stage they are in when they contact OFR they are committed to doing all they can to support these families. www.operationfirstresponse.org

Red Cross: Receive funds for military – family emergencies such as food, temporary lodging, medical needs, money to avoid eviction or utility shut-off, and injured loved one. www.redcross.org

ReserveAid: Is a nonprofit committed to providing financial support to families of Guard/Reserve members for ALL branches which have been called to active duty and experiencing financial hardship. www.reserveaid.org

Salute Inc: The eligibility for the emergency financial assistance program has been temporarily redefined and will require the applicant to be currently service connected or involved in the process of an evaluation for service connection. Provides for OIF/OEF only. www.saluteinc.org

Salute American Heroes: Offers several programs such as Homes For the Wounded, Kids Camps, Family Support Network and Emergency Financial Aid (pays for utilities, mortgage & rent, groceries, car payments including deposits and repairs, home repairs, air travel & lodging, school supplies & clothing, medical bills & co-pays and loans). For assistance or further questions contact (914) 432-5400. www.saluteheroes.org

UnMet Needs: Is a part of VFW and created to provide emergency financial assistance to families of military personnel from ALL branches of service as well as guard/reserve. Funds awarded are provided as a grant. http://www.vfw.org/UnmetNeeds/

USA Cares: Grants made to service providers to cover expenses such as utility and mortgage payments for Post 9/11 military families. http://www.usacares.org/

VA Loan Guaranty Program: Through this program, it's possible to buy a home without a down payment. Applicants obtain the loan from a private lender, and the VA stands behind the loan. www.benefits.va.gov/homeloans/ (888) 768-2132

RETREATS/CAMPS

These camps are a great assistance to many service members transitioning back into the civilian world and/ or with their families. Please take the time to review them all; each are special in their own right and all offer amazing tools, activities and an opportunity to connect with others who have "walked in your shoes."

Adaptive Adventures Military Operations: Provides veterans fitness programs including strength conditioning, skiing, cycling, climbing, paddling, kayaking and retreat camps. http://adaptiveadventures.org/

Boulder Crest Retreat: Provides a rural retreat for wounded, ill and injured service members and their families to reconnect, recover and reintegrate through sports and retreats. www.bouldercrestretreat.org

Breckenridge Outdoor Education Center Military Programs: Hosts a series of events, camps, lessons and activities over the course of the year for recently wounded military personnel and veterans, and their families. Managed by the Breckenridge Outdoor Education Center's Adaptive Ski & Ride School. www.boec.org

Camp C.O.P.E. Provides military families with an unforgettable weekend at Camp C.O.P.E while giving military kids hope, patience and courage. The camp lets them be just kids—again. Through therapeutic interventions, certified therapists teach children and their families how to cope with their changed world due to deployment, injury or loss of a family member as a result of their service to our country. Camp C.O.P.E provides weekend camps across the country FREE of charge to children and families of military personnel. http://campcope.org/

Heal by Choice: Is a phenomenal and much needed retreat for the mothers of deceased warriors. For more information contact www.healbychoiceretreat.com or EMAIL: healbychoiceretreat@gmail.com

Healing Warrior Hearts: Offers retreats for military personnel, veterans and their families which emphasize communication, reintegration and healing from war. http://starfishfound.org/veterans/

Hope for the Warrior: Hosts couples, singles and family wellness retreats as well as caregiver dinners. www.hopeforthewarriors.org

Northwest Natural Horsemanship Center Warrior Family Retreat: Helps service members and their families address transition challenges caused by deployments through equestrian retreats at the Northwest Natural Horsemanship Center. http://nwnhcfamilyfund.org/events/5/warrior-family-retreat/

Outward Bound for Veterans: Helps returning service members and recent veterans readjust to life at home through powerful wilderness courses that draw on the healing benefit of teamwork and challenge through use of the natural world. http://www.outwardbound.org/

Soldier's Heart: Offers holistic healing retreats, international reconciliation journeys, training and public education for service members, veterans and their families affected by post-traumatic stress disorder (PTSD), view the website for a list of contacts working with soldier's heart. http://www.soldiersheart.net **Huge fan of all these holistic healing retreats and techniques.**

TAX INFORMATION

Most large military installations worldwide offer service members and their families' FREE income tax filing assistance through the Volunteer Income Tax Assistance (VITA) program which is sponsored by the IRS. VITA sites have volunteers that are trained by the IRS to provide assistance with some of the more complicated military –specific tax issues, such as combat zones tax benefits. Other great resources are:

Military OneSource: Provides FREE access to the H & R Block at Home online tax filing service for military families. This service allows military members to complete and electronically file federal and up to 3 state tax returns. This is available for active duty service members, National Guard and Reserve, and spouses. You must have a Military OneSource Account. http://www.military.com/discounts/military-onesource-military-discount

IRS Free File: Is a program available to taxpayers whose Adjusted Gross Income (AGI) is $57,000 or less. This program helps you find a Free File company that's best for you out of the numerous companies that participate and offers fillable forms when preparing your own tax returns. http://www.irs.gov

TaxSlayer: Has a FREE military edition for active-duty service members to prepare federal and state returns online. https://www.taxslayer.com/

TurboTax: Offers discounts on its software that's customized for active-duty military and reservists. Service members with pay grades of E1-E5 can get the software for FREE, while pay grades of E6 through all officer grades can get the software at a discounted price. http://www.military.com/discounts/turbotax-military-edition

Taxbrain: Offers a 20% military discount when filing your tax return. Be aware the package price varies depending on answers to their questionnaire. http://www.military.com/discounts/taxbrain-military-tax-filing-discount

VETERANS OF FOREIGN WARS
NO ONE DOES MORE FOR VETERANS.
www.vfw.org

The VFW traces its roots back to 1899 when veterans of the
Spanish-American War (1898) and the Philippine Insurrection
(1899-1902) founded local organizations to secure rights and
benefits for their service:

Since then, the VFW's voice has been instrumental in
establishing the Veterans Administration, creating a GI bill for
the 20th century, the development of the national cemetery
system and the fight for compensation for Vietnam vets exposed
to Agent Orange and for veterans diagnosed with Gulf War
Syndrome. The VFW also has fought for improving VA medical
centers services for women veterans.

Besides helping fund the creation of the Vietnam, Korean
War, World War II and Women in Military Service memorials,
the VFW in 2005 became the first veterans' organization to
contribute to building the new Disabled Veterans for Life
Memorial, which opened in November 2010.

Annually, the nearly 2 million members of the VFW and
its Auxiliaries contribute more than 8.6 million hours of
volunteerism in the community, including participation in Make
A Difference Day and National Volunteer Week.

From providing over $3 million in college scholarships and
savings bonds to students every year, to encouraging elevation
of the Department of Veterans Affairs to the president's cabinet,
the VFW is there.

HEALTH

(Physical, Mental, Emotional and Spiritual)

Health is an important area most families do not discuss, so many resources are never shared. To me this is frustrating, especially at a time when our VA healthcare and benefits are at risk and our families don't know who to ask, where to go and/or fear asking for help. Please share these contacts as lives can and do depend on it.

Angel Flight Soars: Of Atlanta, which provides FREE air transportation to patients for medical treatments not available locally. www.angelflightsoars.com

Asbestos.com – Veterans & Mesothelioma: Offers help to veterans with asbestos – related VA claims and assists with other forms of financial compensation. www.asbestos.com/veterans/

Army Wellness Centers: Provides services designed to promote and sustain healthy lifestyle and improve the overall well-being of soldiers, family members, retirees and Department of the Army Civilians. http://phe. amedd.army.mil/organization/institude/dhpw/pages/ armywellnessCentersOperation.aspx

Blue Star Families – Caregivers Empowering Caregivers:
Offers resources and support for caregivers' concerns,
including prioritizing their needs and setting boundaries
for themselves. Also hosts Caregiver support Workshops at
locations around the country. https://www.bluestarfam.org

Brooke Army Medical Center – Traumatic Brain Injury (TBI):
Provides rehabilitation for wounded veterans of Iraq and
Afghanistan with TBI. Also offers education to DoD and VA
professionals and promotes research.
http://www.bamc.amedd.army.mil/

> **Center for the Intrepid:** Provides rehabilitation for
> wounded veterans of Iraq and Afghanistan who have
> sustained amputation, burns or functional limb loss.
> Also offers education to DoD and VA professionals and
> promotes research in Orthopedics, prosthetics and
> physical/occupational rehabilitation.
>
> **Occupational Therapy:** Promotes soldier readiness,
> healthy living and optimal performance among all DoD
> beneficiaries using occupational therapy principles and
> practices.
>
> **Physical Therapy:** Evaluates neuro-musculoskeletal
> disorders and applies therapeutic exercises and physical
> modalities. Prevents and treats motion impairments and
> offers pain relief.

Care.com/Military: Created in 2006, is one of the largest
and fastest growing service used by families seeking care
provides, providing a place to easily connect with hundreds
of thousands of care provides, share caregiving experiences
and get advice. The company helps families address the
unique lifecycle of care needs that they go through – child
care, senior care, special-needs care, tutoring, pet care,
housekeeping and more. Care.com also provides tools and
information to help families make safer and more informed
decisions throughout the search and hiring process, including

monitored messaging, access to background checks, recorded references, and an online safety guide.
www.care.com/military

Caregiver Support: VA's website dedicated to family caregivers of veterans. It can be an incredibly demanding job and the VA wants you to know you don't have to do it alone. There is a caregiver toolbox and links to find help near home and additional resources. www.caregiver.va.gov

Carson J. Spencer Foundation: Provides suicide prevention programs and supports people bereaved by suicide. This is provided by using innovative methods to address root causes of suicide in schools, homes and businesses. The foundation also assists those copying with pain and grief resulting from the death by suicide of their family, friends or co-workers.
www.carsonjspencer.org

DEERS (Eligibility Verification): www.dmdc.osd.mil/DEERS

DSTRESS Line: Developed by the Marine Corps to provide professional, anonymous counseling for Marines, attached Sailors and families when it's needed most.
http://www.dstressline.com/

The Elizabeth Dole Foundation: Seeks to uplift caregivers by strengthening the service afforded to them through innovation, evidence-based research and collaboration. The **Caregiver Fellow Program** ensures military and veteran caregivers give input to research programs and participate directly in the Foundation's initiative.
http://elizabethdolefoundation.org/

Family Anonymous (FA): FA is not drug, alcohol, or behavior specific. Members focus on themselves—on their recovery from co-dependency and on changing any of their attitudes and behaviors (e.g., denial, enabling, rescuing, controlling, manipulating and a whole range of other crippling actions and emotions) that prevent their own recovery and that of their addicted loved ones. www.familiesanonymous.org

Guard Your Health: A central place for Army National Guard Soldiers and family members to find information and resources on health and medical readiness. http://guardyourhealth.com/

HealthCare.gov – Information for Veterans: Explains the options available to veterans for attaining or changing health care plans under the Affordable Care Act. http://www.healthcare.gov/veterans/

HealtheVet: The DoD My HealtheVet website is designed to allow veterans enrolled in VA health care to check their health records, make and cancel appointments, or refill prescriptions from a computer or tablet. Veterans can send secure e-mails back and forth to their doctors about available treatments without having to go in for an appointment or wait for a phone call. The VA hopes to expand the program and other benefits under one specific app for Android or iPhones as early as summer 2015. https://myhealth.va.gov/index.html

Hearing Aids for Military Retirees: The DoD has sponsored the Retiree-At-Cost Hearing Aid Program (RACHAP) to help retirees purchase hearing aids through the Audiology Clinic at a special government negotiated cost. The hearing aids available through this program are the same state-of-the –art technologies available to active duty service members. The program is open to all military retirees who have hearing loss or tinnitus (ringing in the ears). Dependents of military retirees are not eligible for this program.

Retirees can buy the hearing aids at a significant savings by using the program. Not every medical facility is able to provide the RACHAP program and generally 2 visits are required for you to obtain the hearing aids; one for hearing evaluation and one for your hearing aid fit. Make sure you evaluate the costs associated in to trip to a base as travel overnight expenses are NOT refunded.

Also, retirees may be eligible for hearing aids from the Department of Veterans Affairs (VA) and receive hearing aids from the VA FREE of charge—in most cases there is no costs to the patient. The Audiology Department can provide you with more information about VA services or you can contact the VA directly at (877) 222-8387 or (800) 827-1000.

Dependents of retirees are NOT eligible for hearing aids from military treatment facilities (including RACHAP) or from TRICARE. The family member is eligible for hearing evaluations and the audiologist can provide them with more information.

Hearing Center of Excellence: Promotes the prevention, diagnosis, mitigation, treatment, rehabilitation and research of hearing loss and auditory injury in service members and veterans. http://hearing.health.mil/

International Brain Research Foundation (IBRF): Designs, conducts, supports and oversees research studies in brain injury, disorders and diseases. http://ibrfinc.org/index.htm

My HealtheVet (MHV) : Complete a brief screening tool and get instant feedback. **Spirituality:** Details VA's commitment to offering spiritual care as part of treatment, if it is something veterans want. **Healthy Sleep:** Provides advice on how to maintain healthy sleep that is safe and beneficial to your health. **Smoking Cessation:** Offers help for quitting tobacco for good. **Medications:** Learn how to get the most out of your medications while keeping safe. **Physical Activity:** Allows users to set goals, track their progress, and continue with physical activity that will help benefit their health. **Spinal Cord Injury:** Helps veterans with a spinal cord injury or disorder (SCI/D) and their families. **Research Health:** Browse health information, research a topic and learn more about your general health. **Caregiver Assistance:** Find valuable to provide care. **Common Conditions:** Find basic information for common diseases or conditions and related topics. **Emergency Preparedness:** Teaches how to protect against all types of hazards. Focused on how to develop, practice, and maintain emergency plans that reflect what must be done before, during, and after a disaster to protect people and their property. **Separating from Active Duty:** Encourages healthy living through developing healthier behaviors that last. **Healthy Eating:** Lists tips on developing an "eat wisely plan." https://www.ebenefits.va.gov/ebenefits/nrd

Moving Forward: Operates a FREE, online educational and life coaching program from the VA that teaches problem solving skills to help better handle life's challenges. http://www.wehavemoved.info/

Military Pathways: To help those who may be struggling, the DoD teamed up with various non-profit organizations to help with screening for mental health; to launch Military Pathways (formerly the Mental l Health Self-Assessment Program) the program is available online, over the phone, and at special events held at installations worldwide. It provides FREE, anonymous mental health and alcohol self-assessments are a series of questions that, when linked together, help create a picture of how an individual is feeling and whether they could benefit from talking to a health professional. The primary goals of the program are to reduce stigma, raise awareness about mental health, and connect those in need to available resources.

The self-assessments address depression, post-traumatic stress disorder (PTSD), generalized anxiety disorder, alcohol use and bipolar disorder. After an individual completes a self-assessment, he/she is provided with referral information including services provided through the DoD and Veteran Affairs. www.afterdeployment.dcoe.mil

M.O.V.E. (Weight Management Program For Veterans): Is a national VA program designed to help veterans lose weight, keep it off and improve their health. www.move.va.gov ****This sounds like an interesting program.**

National Association of American Veterans: Assists all veterans and families from WWII to our current military and our severely wounded by helping to access health benefits, improving communication and coordination and collaborating among health agencies, medical professionals, educational organizations and the public communities. http://www.naavets.org

National Center for PTSD: (802) 296-6300 and/or ncptsd@va.gov the website is www.ptsd.va.gov. The VA PTSD Coach app (for smart phones) is www.ptsd.va.gov/public/pages/ptsdcoach.asp. The PTSD Foundation of America is (877) 717-7873 and/or www.ptsdusa.net.

Operation Family Caregiver: Customizes a 16 to 26 week program that is unique to the families of those who have served. www.operationfamilycaregiver.org

Operation Supplement Safety: Is a Defense Department educational campaign that educates the warfighter and healthcare provider on responsible dietary supplement use. While some supplements, such as multivitamins, are generally safe, other supplements can pose a hazard to health and jeopardize careers from adulterants that cause a positive urine drug screen. Body building and weight loss supplements, as well as sexual enhancement and diabetes supplements, are in high-risk categories and should be used with caution if at all. The OPSS website contains videos, fact sheets, FAQs and briefings to help service members make informed, responsible decisions on supplement use, as well as an "Ask the Expert" feature in which service members can directly pose a question to a supplement expert. http://hprc-online.org/dietary-supplements/opss

Powerful Tools for Caregivers: This organization has some excellent tools for caregivers. While it may seem geared toward the aging, the materials available offer excellent insight into self-care. Use the contact button to ask questions about materials that could be targeted to the special needs of your situation. https://www.powerfultoolsforcaregivers.org/

Project C.A.R.E (Comprehensive Aesthetic Restorative Effort): Offers surgical and non-surgical care in an effort to improve physical appearance and restore body functions. http://www.med.navy.mil/sites/nmcsd/patients/pages/projectCARE.aspx

Project SERVE - Sleep Enhancement for Returning Veterans: Offers non-medication insomnia support at no cost for veterans who are experiencing insomnia and suffering depression through a study being conducted by Stanford University and the VA Palo Alto Health Care System. http://projectservesleep.com/

PTSD Awareness: Teaches key information about post-traumatic stress disorder (PTSD), treatment options and support available to veterans and their family members. http://www.ptsd.va.gov/about/PTSD-awarness/

PTSD Coach Online: Is for anyone who needs help with upsetting feelings. Trauma survivors, their families, or anyone coping with stress can benefit. http://www.ptsd.va.gov/apps/ptsdcoachonline/default.htm

Real Warriors – Suicide Prevention Tools for Warriors: Defines warning signs and tools for help. For immediate help, call the Veteran Crisis Line at 800-273-TALK and press 1. You can also send a text message to 838255 and receive confidential support. Find more information http://realwarriors.net/active/treatment/suicidesign.php

Resurrecting Lives Foundation: Assists veterans with traumatic brain injury (TBI) by raising awareness of and funding for research, treatment, advocacy and education of TBI. http://www.resurrectinglives.org/

Supplemental Nutrition Assistance Program (SNAP): Federal nutrition Program administered by state and local agencies provides assistance with purchasing nutritious food for low-income families. (800) 221-5689 http://www.fns.usda.gov/snap/eligibility

Tips & Guidebooks for Families subfolder: Provides assistance to military families in areas of PTSD. www.militaryvetswithPTSD.com

TRICARE (Health and Dental Insurance): http://www.tricare.osd.mil

Unified Behavioral Health Center: Offers a central location for service members, veterans and their families to receive mental health care at no cost. http://wmich.edu/unifiedclinics/behavioral/

United Concordia Dental Insurance: Extra insurance coverage for our military community. (Remember you DO NOT need to be on active duty order to be a part of this extra insurance). http://www.ucci.com

VA & the Affordable Care Act: Answers questions about the Affordable Care Act for veterans and **VA PTSD Coach Online:** Offers simple exercise, tools and strategies for coping with

symptoms of post-traumatic stress disorder. Provided by the VA National Center for PTSD.
http://ptsd.va.gov/apps/ptsdcoachonline/default.htm

VA Compensation: Provides a link to a lists of Diseases associated with health issues after deployments with service members after 1 year of service: http://www.benefits.va.gov/COMPENSATION/claims-postservice-one_year.asp You can also find a full list of eligible diseases on the government website.

VA Mail Order Pharmacy: For information about the National Formulary and the mail order process and benefits go to http://www.pbm.va.gov/PBM/CMOP/VA_mail_order_pharmacy.asp

Veteran Choice Program: The Veterans Access, Choice and Accountability Act is a new law designed to improve health care for veterans. Many veterans will now have the option to receive non- VA health care rather than waiting for a VA appointment or traveling to a VA facility. For more information, visit the Veterans Choice Program at www.va.gov/opa/choiceact/

Veterans of Foreign War (VFW): Offers information to help veterans who are VFW members select a dental plan, find rates, and enroll in the MetLife Preferred Dentist Program (PPD). http://www.vfw.org/MemberBenefits/

Veterans' Family United: Is an all-volunteer nonprofit providing resources for veterans and their families. This organization provides a network of healing, educational and empowerment based tools for veterans and their families. This compilation is an ongoing project. Links with service organizations, therapeutic avenues, pharmaceutical and non-pharmaceutical treatments possibilities, funding sources, volunteer staff and veterans and their families in need are welcome. http://veteransfamiliesunited.org.

Veterans with Multiple Sclerosis: Help for veterans and their families. http://www.va.gov/health/aca/

Veterans Support Center: Is a non-profit 501(c)3 organization, with no government funding. Please visit the website to see the vast array of resources made available for our military community. http://veteransupportcenter.org/

Coordinates with the VA MS Centers of Excellence to support care and support services for veterans with multiple sclerosis and their families. www.va.gov/ms and/or http://www.nationalmssociety.org/living-with-multiple-sclersis/veterans-with-ms

The Warrior Combat Stress Reset Program: Aims to treat combat stress and PTSD symptoms before they worsen and cause dysfunction. Treatment is most effective soon after deployment, when it can prevent further deterioration of function. For symptoms and further information, visit its website at http://www.crdamc.amedd.army.mil

Warrior Navigation and Assistance Program: Provides support and guidance to military (all branches) and civilian health care professionals with treatment, rehabilitation and reintegration of recovering warriors. Examples of services: medical billing and claims, navigating, Tricare, Medicare & veterans' healthcare, assistance in locating specialized medical equipment, connections with resources to meet basic needs (food, shelter, transportation), assistance with transitional care when relocating, and linking with behavioral health resources. www.humana-military.com/wnap

Warrior Wigs: Is a grassroots charity focused on providing customized wigs to military members and their dependents currently undergoing cancer treatment. They are a group of NYC based stylists with a passion for giving back to our military community. They have seen firsthand the power of a great cut and color on one's confidence and spirit and want to be one to provide that gift to those that fight for our freedom. http://www.warriorwigs.com

Women Veterans of America (WVA): Women veterans face their own array of issues after they have finished active duty. WVA was created to be a resource for women veterans and for the families and friends who support them. On this site you can learn about women veterans' health issues, information on military sexual trauma, and the balancing of motherhood with service. The site will provide assistance with understanding military benefits and direct you towards organizations and resources advocating for women veterans. These resources are for current and past members of the military service. www.wvanational.org

CAREGIVER RESOURCES

I personally think caregiving is one of the hardest professions/ life choices someone can make today; even with the resources that are available. Local or online caregiver support groups are helpful in meeting the more-than-full-time challenges of being a family caregiver. Connecting with others who know what you're going through helps and it can alleviate stress for those who are aware and understand where to connect. I hope these listed can ease some of your burden, provide answers and suggestions to questions and provide you a voice and sounding board for your frustrations.

American Veterans with Brain Injuries: Offers weekly online chat groups for veterans and caregivers to share experiences, frustrations, fears and anything else they may have questions/ comments to discuss. www.avbi.org

Her War, Her Voice: Offers retreats for caregivers, raises money to provide counseling for military families, and works with a partner organization, Not Alone, to offer support groups for caregivers, warriors, veterans and military spouses. www.herwarhervoice.com

The National Alliance for Caregiving: Trains and assists civilian and military caregivers. www.caregiving.org

Caregiver.va.gov: The DoD established this national caregiver support program to provide stipend and possibility of health insurance for caregivers of Post-9/11 veterans. It also includes training and support services for caregivers of all veterans, no matter when they served. These programs include:

> **In-home and Community Based Care:** This includes skilled home healthcare, homemaker home health-aide services, community adult day health care and home-based primary care.

> **Respite Care:** Designed to relieve the family caregiver from the constant challenge of caring for a chronically ill or disabled veteran at home, respite services can include in-home care, a short stay in one of VA's community living centers, or an environment designed for adult day health care.

Caregiver Education and Training Programs: VA currently provides multiple training opportunities, including pre-discharge care instruction and specialized caregiver programs for caregivers of veterans with polytrauma such as traumatic brain injury, spinal cord injuries or disorders, and blind rehabilitation. VA also has a family caregiver assistance healthy-living centered on My HealthVet, at www.myhealth.va.gov as well as caregiver information on VA's main health website. Both sites include information on VA and community resources, and caregiver health and wellness.

Health

Other services: VA provides durable medical equipment, prosthetics and sensory aides to improve function, financial assistance with home modification to improve access and mobility, and transportation assistance for some veterans to and from medical appointments.

VA's Post – 9/11 Family Caregiver Program Applications: Posted online at www.caregiver.va.gov the application helps veterans designate a primary family caregiver, and secondary family caregivers if needed. Caregiver support coordinators are stationed at every VA medical center and are available via phone at (877) 222-8387 to assist veterans and their family caregivers with the application process.

Eldercare Locator: The federal Administration on aging has created an Eldercare Locator online at www.eldercare.gov to connect services for older adults and their families. You can also call (800) 677-1116 to speak with an Eldercare information specialist. Use the locator to find community resources for everything from Alzheimer's disease to long term care and transportation. You can fill out an application for caregiver benefits or answers to questions about the program: www.caregiver.va.gov The VA Caregiver Support Line: (855) 260-3274

Revolutionary Veteran Support Network

GallantFew, Inc is a 501(c)3 nonprofit founded in 2010 to provide transition services to military veterans. With specific programs designed around unique populations of veterans, GallantFew's mission is to help every veteran transition to a civilian life filled with purpose and hope.

The biggest threat to a veteran's successful transition is isolation, and the guiding principle for everything GallantFew does is that the best support for a veteran comes from another veteran, one who has previously transitioned successfully and is willing to guide the new veteran through the transition process. GallantFew seeks to create common connections in the same local home-town, so a veteran always has a local Battle Buddy. In this way they overcome the isolation that can lead to many transition programs. GallantFew also strongly believes in developing "Response-ability" and coaches veterans on how to control their ability to respond positively to life situations.

The Darby Project (www.darbyproject.org) serves US Army Ranger veterans; the Raider Project (www.raiderproject.org) serves Marine Special Operations and ground combat troops; Wings Level (www.wingslevel.org) serves US Air Force veterans; and GallantFew ensures veterans not included in these programs also receive individual support while looking for opportunities to establish programs with other categories of veterans.

Other significant programs include The Spartan Pledge (www.spartanpledge.com) which is an antisuicide platform based on the buddy system; and Run Ranger Run (www.runrangerrun.com), an annual awareness and fundraising event.

For more information please visit www.gallantfew.org or call 817-567-3293.

MILITARY DISCOUNTS

TRAVEL

There are so many beautiful places, great savings and great opportunities military families can use while traveling. With a little research you will be pleasantly surprised at what is available, offered and the amount of money you can/will save. For all Discounts and Travel discounts veterans must provide a CURRENT military ID card and/or veteran logo on their driver's license. Remember there is also a long list of discounts and travel resources in my first edition of Operation Military Resources.

Anheuser Bush Amusement Parks: Discount may vary. ****Used this in 2014, had a great time.**

Armed Forces Vacation Clubs: Offers military families huge vacation discount deals. https://www.afvclub.com/

Busch Gardens: Offers a one complimentary admission for members of the military and 3 direct dependents; must have a current military ID card. ****Used this in 2014; had a great time.**

Campgrounds and More: http://www.4militaryfamilies.com/militaryvacationspots.html

Disneyland: Discounts offered ONLY at tickets purchased at installation MWR's and prices vary per date and length of visit.

Disney Resorts: Discount may vary.

Easy Military Travel: Can assist with all your travel needs. Provides assistance with vacations, emergency travel, or just flying with a friend. The company finances 100% of your travel all with no money down. The site is a travel now and pay later. http://www.easymilitarytravel.com/index.php

Guides to Military Travel: Provides information about all types of military lodging, cruises, flights and much more. http://www.guidetomilitarytravel.com

Florida Military Museum: The Museum and Library is dedicated to preserving and displaying military artifacts and memorabilia while educating the public about our nation's military heritage. It is the largest military museum in SW Florida. All of the artifacts have been donated or loaned by the military, government and individuals. The museum is at 4820 Leonard St., Cape Coral, Fla. It is open 9 a.m. – 5 p.m. Monday – Sunday. Admission is FREE. www.swfmm.org

Groupon: Offers a "Getaway Section" that provides vacation packages to locations like China, Peru, Bahamas and other tourists spots. http://groupon.com

Hotels/Motels: All offer a discount, it will vary by location. **I ask all the time and get great discounts.**

Installation Lodging Contact Information:
Listed links and contact information about installation lodging and recreation facilities.

- **ARMY: (800) 462-7691**
  http://www.armymwr.com/portal/travel

- **Air Force: (888) 235-6343**
  http://dtic.mil/perdiem/af_lodgi.html

- **NAVY: (800) 628-9466**
  http://www.navy-lodge.com/

Military Lodging Information:

- **Air Force Inns: (888) AF-LODGE**
  http://www.militarylodging.us/

- **ARMY Central Reservation Center:**
  http://www.militarylodging.us/

- **In US: (800) GO-ARMY1**

  - **In Germany: 01-30-81-7065**

  - **In Korea: 00-78-11-893-0828**

  - **In Italy: 16-78-70555**

- **Navy Lodges Worldwide: (800) NVAY-INN or (301) 654-1795** http://www.navy-lodge.com/

- **Marine Corps Lodging:**
  http://usmc-mccs.org/lodging/index.cfm

Military Hotel Lodging:

- **Armed Forces Recreation Centers-Europe:**
  http://www.afrceurope.com

- **Hale Koa Hotel, Hawaii:**
  http://www.armymwr.com/shades/index.html

- **The New Sanno Hotel, Japan:**
  http://www.thenewsanno.com/home.html

- **Keystone, Colorado Rocky Mountain Blue:**
  http://www.rockymountainblue.com

- **Armed Forces Vacation Club:** http://www.
  armymwr.com/portal/travel/lodging/patronlinks/
  sav.asp

Leisure Travel Services (MWR): Great discount prices for travel/vacations i.e., cruises, lodging, tours, entertainment & Sports, Disney & Amusement Parks, Armed Forces Vacation Club, Government Vacation Rewards (586)-282-0973. https://www.afvclub.com/military_mwr

Military To Go: Travel savings for military families and the soldier. www.militarytogo.com

Military Travel: Great site for Space A Travel and Lodging. http://www.military.com/Travel/Home/

MWR: Offers discounts in lodging and cruises. Contact them through your local military installation. https://www.afvclub.com/military_mwr

Rental Cars: Companies like Budget, Avis, and Enterprise etc..., offer military discounts. ****I use Budget all the time and they have been very generous and offer a great discount.**

Ripley's Attractions and Museums: Discount will vary.

SATO Vacations Europe: Discount military travel. http://www.europe.satovacations.com

Sea World: For years SeaWorld (which owns Bush Gardens, Adventure Island, Sesame Place and Aquatica) has offered FREE admission to active duty military families. On a seasonal basis, the park also offers a generous discount to students, veterans, and teachers. You can find out more at the website: Waves of Honor. http://www.militarydisneytips.com/index.html

Sesame Park Place: One day complimentary admission for members of the military and 3 direct dependents. http://sesameplace.com/en/langhorne/

SPACE-A-TRAVEL: Military planes (and planes contracted by the military) have mission assignments throughout the world and will offer empty seats to eligible passengers. Space-A is an awesome way to travel safely and at massive savings. Passengers can't reserve seats; available seats are offered to register passengers before the flight. For military families traveling on a military flight all over the world is one of the great benefits offered; but you must be flexible. Military flights are (sometimes) unpredictable and subject to delays and cancellations. You'll need to be ready both financially and emotionally to change your plans at a moment's notice. But for many Spaces-A passengers, traveling to places like Hawaii, Alaska, Europe, or Japan at no cost is worth the effort. You can get a list of eligibility and regulations from the current Space-A book at www.militaryliving.com **LOVE this program...I hope to use it again in the future.**

Useful sites for Space-A travelers:

> **Baseops.net:** Flight planning information for military space available travel.
> http://www.baseops.net/spacetravel/

> **John D's Military Space-A-Travel Pages:** Provides a variety of information about space a travel.
> http://www.spacea.net/

> **Military Hops:** Is a site dedicated to being a premier index of information about space-a military flights.
> www.militaryhops.com

Take a Hop: Is a private website supporting eligible DoD space-available travelers with easy sign ups. www.takeahop.com

The Space A Experience Demystified: Download an information guide to traveling Space A brought to you buy My Military Concierge and Army Wife Network. www.mymilitaryconcierge.com

Travel Apps: Mobile apps such as **TripIt** can keep all of your hotel, flight and car rental reservations in one handy "digital pocket."

TravelZoo: Tons of savings and some of the best deals on the web, arriving is a weekly e-mail customized for your location. You can also browse the site, which features vacation packages, airfare, hotels, cruises, car rentals and even local deals to restaurants and other places. Another perk; the price listed is the price you pay—all fees included. If you're flexible about travel dates, it's one of the best options. http://www.travelzoo.com/ ****I use these travel discounts all the time.**

Vacation for Vets: Are you are planning ahead of time for a vacation and would like to stay at a resort but fear the cost? Than this foundation may be for you; at iHoots.com with a deposit (non-refundable) of $75 Active Duty/$100 for veterans you can book at several locations throughout U.S. for a FREE 7-day/6-Night stay. It is recommended you send in your application 6-weeks in advance to allow for processing. For further details, eligibility and the application go to www.ihoot.org/vacation-for-vets ****I learned about this program in FEB 2015; sounds like a great program.**

Vacation for Veterans: Provides a FREE week of vacation lodgings to Purple Heart Medal recipients from the Iraq and Afghanistan Campaigns. http://www.vacationsforveterans.org/

Veteran Holidays – The Vacations for Veterans from Veterans Holidays (VETO): Is a "Space Available" program that offers military and other Department of Defense affiliated personnel the opportunity to enjoy vacations at popular destinations around the world – for the incredibly low price of just $349 USD per unit, per week. http://www.veteransholidays.com

GENERAL MILITARY DISCOUNTS

For all discounts the veteran community must provide a CURRENT military ID card and/or veteran logo on current driver's license. Do you have an amazing military discount to share? Share it with me on Twitter at @OpMilResources or my Facebook page at http://www.facebook.com/OperationMilitaryResources

APPLEBEE's: Most are aware of the generous FREE meal offered on veterans day by this awesome restaurant but in several locations (check with yours) in 2014 they began offering 20% daily discount for military families; this DOES NOT include alcohol beverages. ****Thank you Applebee's… very generous and much appreciated.**

Apple Military and Government Store: The iconic brand offers special pricing for military and government personnel online. http://www.apple.com/r/store/government

Auto Zone/NAPA/O'Reilly Auto Parts: Offers vary from locations but is generally from 10-20% off total order. ****I am a frequent buyer at AutoZone….very generous store and great customer service.**

Bed & Breakfasts – B&B industry celebrates the sacrifices offered by vets by offering FREE rooms on or around Veterans Day. ****Stayed in some great ones over by Traverse City.** http://www.betterwaytostay.com/bbs-for-vets.

Bodybuilding.com Military Discount: Offers 10% off purchases to verify military, veterans, and their families through Troop ID. Eligible customers who register with ID.me receive additional 3.3% cash back. http://go.id.me/1tUpXU5

Cirque de Soleil: Offers up to 50% off of their shows; call ahead to reserve your ticket. Most places that have live shows in Las Vegas offer military discounts. ****They sell out so quickly...I hope to see them sometime soon.**

Coffee Beans and Tea Leaf: Offers a 20% discount on top of sales, coupons & clearance

Dell Military Appreciation Program: To recognize military service, Dell created a military and veteran discount program. Verified service members, veterans, and their families get 10% off purchases as well as 5.3% cash back if they are registered. http://go.id.me/1AUePar

HP Military Discount: Offers a 20% discount and free shipping on many products. Plus registered ID.me members receive additional 1.3% cash back on purchases. http://go.id.me/1FBHyF3

Home Depot/Lowe's: Offers 10-20% off total order year around. ****Thank you Lowes and Home Depot...I know I greatly appreciate your support.**

ITT Office at Base: Will provide (most will) a list of the local attractions that offer military discounts. For example, the

ITT Office in Las Vegas provides free tickets to various local shows and attractions with a list to other discounts and sites of interest.

JCPenny Store: Offers 50% off photos and on Veterans Day offers 10% off total orders.. ****This was very helpful the day I used it. I wish they would offer the discount every day or at least once a week like Old Navy does.**

ManUP: Is a service designed to help veterans "re-claim their old self" with expert nutritional information, team based workouts and competitions, and individualized coaching. Service members and veterans are eligible for 40% off plans. http://go.id.me/txZC115

Microsoft Military and Government Discount Program: Active duty military members and veterans are eligible for special discounts on most products. Id.me users get additional 2% cash back on purchases. https://id.me/military

Military.com: Is a great resource of information of discounts offered to the military community. http://military.com/discounts/ ****This is an awesome site; I visit there all the time for information and great military news media updates.**

Motel 6: Starting in 2013. Launched a discount program with The American Legion to offer Legionnaires and Sons of The American Legion (SAL) members discounted rates on Motel 6 and Studio 6 room reservations across the United States and Canada. The discounted Program offers a 15% discount on their rooms, whenever they choose to travel. Standard amenities include FREE local phone calls, no long-distance access charges, FREE morning coffee, Wi-Fi Internet access and an expanded cable lineup. All Motel 6 properties welcome pets, and most locations offer swimming pools and guest laundry facilities.

To reserve a room and activities the 15% discount, Legionnaires and SAL members can log on to motel6.com and enter the access code CP565474 during the booking process, or visit the Member Discount Programs page on the Legion's website – www.legion.org/discounts/travel - and enter the access code. Members can also use their discount when booking a room via the reservation line at (800) 4 – MOTEL6. www.motel6.com

Movie Theaters: There are several movie theaters that offer military discounts to our military community. Be sure to check with yours. Regal's is the company in my location and they offer 10% off ticket price. ****Very generous and much appreciated.**

Netsonic Web Hosting: Is honored to show their support and appreciation by offering all active duty and veteran Soldiers, Sailors, Airmen, Marines and Coast Guardsmen with FREE web hosting services for 6 months or 15% off to help service men and women launch, maintain , and grow their own businesses. http://www.netsonic.net/veterans-hosting-discount.php

Old Navy and Michaels Crafts: Offer discounts one day a week; check your local store for the day specified. ****Very generous and much appreciated.**

Overstock.com "Club O" Membership: Quietly, the online retailer has setup a program that offers FREE "Club O" membership to verified service members and veterans. After verifying eligibility current and former service members receive free shipping and 5% store credit on all Overstock.com . http://go.id.me/1AUcNqV . ****They have some great products at great discounts on top of the military discounts.**

Payless Shoes: Offers a 20% discount on top of sales, coupons & clearance. ****Very generous and much appreciated.**

PowerLabNutrition.com: Offers 20% off military discount.

Protect America Military Discount: Mention the promo code "militaryAwards" while getting a home security system from Protect America to get $5 off your monthly bill and a 10-25% discount off your home security. (800) 951-5190 http://www.protectamerica.com/

SkyRange Military Discount: Is offering a $25 HughesNet satellite internet service to veterans and members of the US military. http://www.skyrange.net/military-discounts

Southwest Airlines: I have been told they have amazing deals if you call the 800 number. ****I personally get better deals through Travelzoo. But I said I would list them for a friend.**

TentsforTroops.org: Offers RV and camping sites to active military and their families for FREE. They have 250+ Parks across 45 states participating and more added each week. Some parks offer FREE Cabins as well. ****Sounds interesting...**

Thompson Cigar Military Discount: Is the oldest mail order cigar delivery brand in the country, they are popular in the military and veteran community. Thompson's offers 10% off and free shipping on all orders for military, veterans, and first responders. http://go.id.me/1sfGgrVN

Veterans Day Free Meals and Discounts: An updated list from 2015. http://themilitarywallet.com/veterans-day-free-meals-and-discounts/

VeteranDiscounts.com: A searchable database of discounts from retail establishments. http://veteransdiscounts.com/

VetTix: Founded and managed by veterans, VetTix is a non-profit organization that collects donated tickets from major league sports teams, venues, event organizers, and military supporters in order to give away FREE tickets to active military, veterans, and their families. When demand is greater than the supply of FREE tickets, the site holds a lottery between verified users in order to determine who will receive the free tickets. Verified Troop ID members can use their Troop ID login to prove their eligibility for the program. http://www.vettix.org. **This is a favorite organization of mine. They offer so much to our military community.**

Reminder, if you don't currently have Operation Military Resources VOL I make sure to get your copy today for over 22 pages of discounts, and travel information and tools not listed in this edition. Order your copy at www.MilitaryResourceBooks.com.

FINANCIAL RESOURCES

One of the life lessons I wish I could change (and there are a few) is how I handled money. Not only how I spent it over the years but the lack of investing and planning for "down the road." The way this country/economy is being run and with all the uncertainty of our social security, our younger generations need to think of their futures. While visiting different bases I am always surprised at how young our service members are. Please take the time, review these resources and ask yourself…. "What will be supporting me and my family 40 years from today or when you retire."

Armed Forces Crossroads: Covers benefits, deployment, relocation and other issues. www.afcrossroads.com

Armed Forces Legal Assistance: Includes a search tool to help you find legal-assistance offices at nearby bases. http://legalassistance.law.af.mil

Better Business Bureau: Helps you check out businesses in your new hometown or online and works to resolve complaints, BBB Military Line (www.bbb.org/military) specializes in consumer alerts, financial education and resources for members of the military. www.bbb.org

ClearPoint Credit Counseling Solutions: Offers budget, housing, and debt-counseling resources. www.clearpointcreditcounselingsolutions.org

Consumer Financial Protection Bureau Service Members': Includes resources specifically designed to help members of the military plan for the future and protect their finances. www.consumerfinance.gov/servicemembers

Defense Credit Union Council: Includes contact information for credit unions on base and other financial information for service members. www.dcuc.org

Defense Financial and Accounting Service: Includes information about active military and retiree pay, benefits and savings. www.dfas.mil ****This is very useful information to understand and plan for in advance.**

Department of Veterans Affairs SGLI: This site offers in-depth information about service members' group life insurance. www.insurance.va.gov/sgliSite/default.htm ****A smart thing to understand and make your spouse and children aware.**

Investor Protection Trust: Provides information about investing and protecting your money, including an excellent guide to help you get started in investing. Look for special education resources for the military. www.investorprotection.org ****Make sure you trust and feel comfortable with your choices.**

IRS Armed Forces Tax Guide: Explains special tax rules that can benefit military personnel. www.irs.gov ****All military families need to be aware of the tax rules and write offs.**

Kiplinger.com: Provides timely advice and information to help with all areas of personal finances, from saving and investing to insurance, taxes, homeownership and financial planning. http://kiplinger.com

MyArmyBenefits: Includes information about military pay and benefits, transition information and tax rules. http://myarmybenefits.us.army.mil ****Great site full of useful information.**

Military.com: Focuses on pay and benefits, financial issues, preparing for deployment and transitioning out of the military. ***A personal fan favorite site of mine.** http://military.com

Military Homefront: This Department of Defense website highlights resources and benefits for military families. www.militaryhomefront.dod.mil ****Another favorite site.**

MilitaryMoney.com: Offers advice on all aspects of personal finance for military families, plus links to discount and support programs. www.militarymoney.com ****Provides great useful information.**

MilitaryOneSource.com: Is a clearinghouse for information related to all things military, including deployment, legal rights and finances. www.militaryonesource.com

MilitarySaves.org: Focuses on strategies for building savings and reducing debt, and includes inspirational stories from service members who make savings a priority. The site also highlights special programs during military saves week (last week in February). www.militarysaves.org ****Great site with great information.**

MyMoney.gov: Includes helpful information from a variety of government resource about budget, taxes, homeownership and credit, and how to avoid scams. www.mymoney.gov

National Association of Insurance Commissioners: This site focuses on insurance issues for members of the military, and

includes contact information for insurance regulators.
www.naic.org/consumer_military_insurance.htm

National Military Family Association: Features resources
to help families make the most of their benefits prepare for
deployment and cope with financial issues.
www.militaryfamily.org **Great site and information.**

North American Security Administrators Association: Includes
links to state securities regulators, tips on avoiding scams and
other helpful information for investors.
www.nasaa.org

SaveandInvest.org: Alerts military families to active scams,
includes advice on saving and investing and provides resources
for checking out advisers. www.saveandinvest.org

The Securities and Exchange Commission: Military site offers
warnings about scams targeting members of the military as
well as general investor education and tips on how to check out
a broker. www.sec.gov/investor/military.shtml

TSP.gov: Features details about the Thrift Savings Plan for
military personnel. www.tsp.gov **Fan favorite and our family
uses this.**

U.S. Department of Justice: Provides details on special legal
rights for members of the military and veterans.
www.servicemembers.gov **A site all military should be
aware of.**

VA Loans: This Department of Veteran Affairs site includes
detailed information on VA loans. www.homeloans.va.gov

ADDITIONAL RESOURCES

You'll find helpful information about benefits and support for military families at these sites.

Air Force: www.afcommunity.af.mil

Army: www.myarmyonesource.com

Army Reserve: www.arfp.org

Coast Guard: www.uscg.mil/worklife

Marine Corps: www.usmc-mccs.org

Navy: www.nffsp.org

National Guard:
www.nationalguard.mil, www.jointservicessupport.org

Reserve Affairs: http://ra.defense.gov

Mission/Prime Objective: To properly arm and protect all military veterans (including those currently serving) contemplating going into or already in business from the ravages/pitfalls of real world capital financing by providing free to all veterans the:

- First complete business financing guide providing practical and down- to-earth coverage for every available funding option;
- First detailed how-to business financing guide leveling the playing field by examining how it works in the real world;
- First "from the trenches manual" road map providing financial tactics with step by step descriptions on how, what, when, and why to avoid the "potholes" within the processes and system;
- First small business financial guide providing in-depth pros and cons for each and every financial option;
- First Book authored by a well recognized expert authority on the entire array of business financing options and entrepreneurship;
- First financing guide where every chapter has been reviewed pre publication by other recognized financial experts/professionals in all genres
- The Source/Solution

The Ultimate Financing Guide is the "complete package" – most authoritative in-depth treatise dedicated to tactical financial decision-making ever written/published covering the entire array of small business options in a practical, no nonsense style – leveling the playing field by explaining every facet as to how it works in the real world!

Learn how to acquire your copy today from Operation Veteran Empowerment http://www.ultimatefinancingguide.com

ENTREPRENEUR/VETREPENEUR

Along with skills developed while serving their country; our service members (and their dependents) acquire many life skills that add to being perfect individuals to own their own business. To assist with goals in this endeavor make sure to utilize the many resources available to start and expand your business.

American Corporate Partners (ACP): A great program our military community needs to be aware of; they supply a veteran a mentor that can assist an entrepreneur in connecting them with potential investors, advisors, and maybe even customers. www.acp-usa.org/

American Dream U: A non-profit dedicated to helping our military get the education and access to resources they need to find their dream job or start a business of their own. Check out their FREE "Business Accelerator" online course helping aspiring entrepreneurs who have an idea for business, but need a plan and framework to successfully start a company. http://americandreamu.org/

Angel Investment Groups Who Support Veterans – *Hivers and Strivers:* Is an angel investment group funding early-stage investments in start-up companies founded and run by graduates of the US Military Academies. The company generally invests $250,000 to $1 million in a single round. A company seeking larger rounds can actively look to other investor groups in the Hivers and Strivers network for additional funds. Their goal is to support veteran entrepreneurs through a successful exit with a return 10 times the initial investment. Veterans can learn more about H&S and complete an application on website. http://www.hiversandstrivers.com/

Building Bright Futures Fund: This resource is a grant fund to assist when blended with other financing sources to enable programs to start, relocate, expand, or improve their physical facility and accessibility. Learn more at http://business.usa.gov/program/building-bright-futures-fund

Entrepreneurship Bootcamp for Veterans (EBV): The EBV National Program offers cutting edge, experiential training in entrepreneurship and small business management to Post 9/11 veterans with disabilities and their family members. http://ebv.vets.syr.edu/

FedMine: A federal market research and business intelligence service/site that provides real time federal spending data and contractor information source. They serve veteran contractors nationwide including the US Veteran Administration. http://www.fedmine.com/

InclineHq.com: Teaches military veterans the tools they need to become a junior programmer. www.InclineHq.com

Loans and Grants Search Tool: Site helps you search and identify what government financing programs may be available to help start your business, go to "access financing" at Wizard from BusinessUSA. www.business.usa.gov/

Keep in mind SBA and BusinessUSA DO NOT provide grants to start or expand your business. Some Federal grants do exist but are ONLY available to certain non-commercial organizations.

National Disabled Veterans Assistance Foundation: 28202 Cabot Rd #300, Laguna Niguel, CA 92677. PHONE: (949) 365-5750 and/or tony@dvaf.org

The National Veteran Small Business Coalition (NVSBC): Is an organization for all veterans' owned firms respecting federal market acquisition and procurements is now a strategic partner and supporter. http://www.nvsbc.org/

The National Veteran Business Development Council (NVBDC): Is a veteran-owned Business Certification Program created to ensure national level credible and reliable certifying processes for properly validating veteran business ownership and control. http://www.nvbdc.org

Operation Endure & Grow: Is an expansion on the "Boot Camp" and provides high quality training, networking, mentoring to support military community. http://whitman.syr.edu/EndureAndGrow/About/

Operation Veteran Empowerment: This is an awesome tool that all veteran business owners NEED to review and learn. http://www.operationveteranempowerment.com

SBA Women's Business Centers (WBC): Represent a national network of nearly 100 educational centers throughout the US and its territories, which are designed to assist women in starting and growing small businesses. WBC seek to "level the field" for women entrepreneurs, who still face unique obstacles in the business world. SBA's Office of Women's Business Ownership (OWBO) oversees the WBC network, which provides entrepreneurs (especially women who are economically or socially disadvantaged) comprehensive

Entrepreneur

training and counseling on a variety of topics in several languages. http://www.sba.gov/tools/local-assistance/wbc).

Score's Veteran Fast Launch Initiative:
http://www.score.org/vetsfastlaunch/

Service Disabled Veteran Owners Small Business Network (NCA): http://sdvosbnetwork.org/

Set Aside Alert: A federal government contract information service for small businesses, minority-owned and women-owned businesses, veteran and SDV – owned businesses, SBA 8(a) certified companies and HUBzone businesses is a partner/sponsor. http://www.setasidealert.com/

StreetShares, Inc.: Created by American Legion and other Organizations is an online social lending marketplace, veterans business campaign. StreetShares.com provides a new way for small business owners to get commercial loans, funded by the direct investments of individuals through an interactive auction. www.streetshares.com

Task Force for Veterans' Entrepreneurship (Vet Force): Is a non-profit organization whose primary mission is to advocate for the implementation of legislation, programs, and regulations to increase contracting and employment opportunities for veteran and service disabled veteran business owners. www.vetsgroup.org

Techstars Patriot Bootcamp: Provides veterans, active duty service members and their spouses with the tools and resources to be successful entrepreneurs. PBC is a national program designed to engage, inspire, and mentor military veterans and their spouses to start, innovate, and scale the next generation of business leaders in technology. PBC provides FREE education training in entrepreneurial and business skills as well as mentoring to participants.
http://www.techstars.com/patriotbootcamp/

Techstars RisingStar Program: Extends technology company startup opportunities to veterans and others. www.techstars.com/risingstars/

UnitedUs.com: Empowers military families and their supporting entities; UniteUS is a free place to connect veterans, service members, and Military Families to impact resources and opportunities in their local communities. These opportunities include connecting with local veteran non-profits, jobs, events, services, peers as well as civilian supporters.

There are thousands of organizations and millions of peers and supporters dedicated to providing support and United US can guide you on where to start with their interactive mapping tools, you can find everything you will need to get started with mentors, local veteran organizations, to real-time local career postings. www.unitedus.com

Veteran Business Outreach Program (VBOP): Is designed to provide entrepreneur development services such as business training, counseling and mentoring, and referrals for eligible veterans owning or considering starting a small business. The SBA has 15 organizations participating in this cooperative agreement and serving as Veterans Business Outreach Centers (VBOC). https://www.sba.gov/ and/or http://business.usa.gov/ program/veterans-business-outreach-program-vbop

Veteran Entrepreneur Portal: Information for VOSB and SDVOSB to include starting and expanding a business, Vets first contracting program, Acquisition support, strategic outreach, Small and Veteran Business Programs and Small Business Administration resources. Contact Jonah J. Czerwinski, VA Director of Innovation Initiative at Jonah.Czerwinski@va.gov and/or (866) 584-2344. http://www.va.gov/osdbu/entrepreneur

Entrepreneur

Veteran Entrepreneurship Program: Empowering Disabled Veterans: The VEP provides a rigorous entrepreneurial and development opportunity for serviced disabled veterans and those who have uniquely distinguished themselves in the military. VEP is designed for veterans interested in starting a new business as a means to financial independence and for veterans who have an existing business for which they would like to expand. POC: (352) 273-0330 and/or vep@warrington.ufl.edu or http://warrington.ufl.edu/centers/cei/outreach/vep/

Veteran and Military Business Owners Association: http://vamboa.org

VictorySpark: Exposes veteran-initiated start-ups to a national group of mentors and investors. http://gan.co/members/view/victory-spark

WAVE' – Women as Veteran Entrepreneurs – "Catch the Wave:" http://www.thewave.us.com/

Women Veterans Business Center: A primary national women veteran's organization. http://www.womenveteransbusinesscenter.org/contactus.html

Women Veterans Igniting the Spirit of Entrepreneurship: This program is open to all female veterans, active duty female service members and female partner spouses of active duty service members and veterans who share the goal of launching and growing a sustainable business venture. Participants may be from any branch of the military and any era of service. For information you can check out website or Email. http://whitman.syr.edu/vwise/about.aspx

VetBizCentral

501 S. Averill Ave.
Flint, MI 48506

vetbizcentral.org
810-767-8387

Michigan POC
Matt Sherwood

MISSION STATEMENT

VetBizCentral's mission is to help veterans develop new businesses and further the growth of existing veteran-owned businesses. We educate, mentor and offer business development services, including opportunities for state and federal procurement.

ABOUT VETBIZCENTRAL

Established in 2005, VetBizCentral is a non-profit 501(c)3 VBOC. Funded by the Small Business Administration, we offer services to Illinois,Indiana, Michigan, Minnesota, Ohio and Wisconsin. We assist all honorably discharged Veterans, Reservists and National Guard.

SERVICES AVAILABLE

Business Planning
Entrepreneurial Training
Franchising
Networking Opportunities
Mentoring Programs and Activities

Workshops
Conferences
Procurement Counseling
Advocacy Services
Financial Planning

REGION V

Veteran **B**usiness **O**utreach **C**enter

Illinois - Indiana - Michigan - Minnesota - Ohio - Wisconsin

Funded in part through a cooperative agreement with the U.S Small Business Administration.
All opinions, conclusions or recommendations expressed are those of the author(s) and do not necessarily reflect the views of the SBA.

To find local services for your state go to: <u>VetBizCentral.org</u>

STATE-SPECIFIC MILITARY RESOURCES

The material I generally share is about organizations that provide assistance no matter where you are stationed or live; but just as important are the state-specific resources that provide fast, efficient assistance for service members and their families living ONLY in the specific state listed. As there are many to choose from, I have only listed a couple for each state. This in no way dictates the importance of one organization over another. I may not be aware of your organization at the printing of this book. Plus I do not have enough space to list them all. Feel free to email me any resources you would like to see promoted and shared on my social media sites, website and any possible future editions.

ALABAMA:

Alabama Veteran Government Job Link:
https://joblink.alabama.gov/ada/default.cfm

Lakeshore Foundation: Serves those with physical disabilities and provides access to exercise and recreational opportunities. This program includes a number of weekend-long camps that bring injured military personnel and their families from across the country to Alabama. Each camp, referred to as an operation, is offered at no charge for the participants. Activities include Operation Rise & Conquer, an outdoor adventure weekend held at Lake Martin, Operation DownHome, a weekend camp for injured service men and women as well as their families; Operation Night Vision, a camp specifically designed for injured troops who have suffered blindness or visual impairment; Operation Alpha for servicemen and women who have sustained traumatic brain injuries; Operation Refocus brings together past participants to look at how participation in LIMA FOXTROT shaped their lives once they return home from Lakeshore and Operation Endurance, which provides daily fitness programs to recently injured military personnel returning home from Alabama. http://www.lakeshore.org/

National Guard Family Readiness: The National Guard Family Program strives to make sure that you and your family are prepared for whatever may be ahead of you; no matter what phase or transition of military life you are currently experiencing. http://www.alabama.gov/

Operation Grateful Heart: Alabama's program ensures all military personnel and their families receive appropriate recognition, tangible support, and neighborly care. https://ebenefits.va.gov/ebenefits/nrd

Veterans Upward Bound Programs: The Veterans Upward Bound Program (VUB) is a free program dedicated to providing eligible veterans with numerous educational and counseling services. http://www.gadsdenstate.edu/college-life/veterans-upward-bound.php and http://nacee.net/programs/veterans-upward-bound/

ALASKA:

Alaska Housing: AHFC is proud to offer several loan programs in honor of our veterans. Qualified veterans may purchase owner-occupied single family residences

and with certain restrictions, a duplex, triplex or fourplex. Long-term financing is also available for owner-built, newly constructed, single family homes.
http://www.ahfc.us/buy/loan-programs/vets/

Fisher House Comfort Homes – Joint Base Elmendorf-Richardson: Provides FREE temporary housing for families of patients receiving medical care at major military and VA medical centers. http://www.akfisherhouse.org

MyArmyBenefits: Alaska offers special benefits for its military Service members and veterans. These benefits include the Permanent Dividend Fund (PFD), Military Credit toward State Retirement, Property Tax Exemptions, State Employment Preferences, Education and Tuition Assistance, Veterans Land Discount/Purchase Preference, Vehicle Tags, as well as Hunting and Fishing License privileges. Eligibility for some benefits may depend on residency, military component and veteran disability status.
http://myarmybenefits.us.army.mil/Home.html

Pro Bono Legal Resources: This is an awesome link for legal aid pro bono work for not only Alaska but for all states. It an amazing list to have on hand especially if you're a service member or military family who is PCSing continuingly.
http://www.va.gov/ogc/docs/pro_bono_resources.pdf

ARIZONA:

Arizona Coalition for Military Families: Builds Arizona's statewide capacity to serve and support all service members, veterans, their families and communities.
www.Arizonacoalition.org

Veterans Fire Corps (Part of Veterans Green Job): CURRENT OPPORTUNITIES: All programs are operated in partnership with local conservation corps and Veterans Green Jobs.

State Resources

There are currently three corps, the **California Conservation Corps (CA only), Southwest Conservation Corps (CO, NM), Arizona Conservation Corps (AZ, NM) and the Student Conservation Association (nationwide)** that are running Veterans Fire Corps programs. Please contact these programs directly for additional information about specific program opportunities. VFC programs operate in Arizona, California, Colorado, New Mexico, and Arizona during the winter, spring, summer and fall season. For additional details and specific information, click on the links below that will take you to individual websites for each corps.

For more information on programs in Arizona and Southern New Mexico, in partnership with the Arizona Conservation Corps, http://www.azcorps.org/join/

For more information on programs in Arizona and South Dakota, in partnership with the Student Conservation Association, http://www.thesca.org/

SaddleBrooke Troop Support: Supports Arizona military personnel and their families while home or deployed, as well as disabled and hospitalized veterans at the Tucson VA Hospital. www.Saddlebrooke-troop-support.com

ARKANSAS:

Arkansas Freedom Fund: Offers rehabilitation and recreational sporting events and programs designed to get military wounded veterans outdoors and active during recovery and reintegration. http://arkansasfreedomfund.org/

Arkansas SBDC: Developed Arkansasveteran.com as a one-stop virtual veterans center, providing information about health, education, employment, entrepreneurship and family issues. This portal links federal, state and local resources available to veterans. Several colleges and universities have joined in this initiative and offer free online courses to veterans through the site. The Arkansas SBDC also joins other veterans' organizations to provide transition assistance for deployment as well as for transition back to civilian life. http://asbtdc.org/

Operation Renewal: Has created a team to introduce a full range of outreach services to assist with the divorce rate among their military community. Support services for the spouses of deployed troops to a weekend retreat for military couples—to help NW Arkansas military families endure the hardships that military life often imposes on soldier's returning from war. http://oprenewal.org.sg/

CALIFORNIA:

Institute for Military Personnel, Veterans, Human Rights & International Law & AMVETS Legal Clinic: Offers pro bono representation to military personnel and veterans with issues ranging from discharge upgrades, Traumatic Service Group Life Insurance appeals, VA benefit appeals and issues arising under the Service members Civil relief Act (SCRA). www. chapman.edu/research-and-institutions/military-law-institute

Our Heroes' Journey: Has an "Adopt a Hero" Program that focuses on military families and service members who may need help with groceries, gas cards, diapers and other daily necessities. www.ourheroesjourney.com

The CA –Dept of Veteran Affairs: CDVA offers a wide range of assistance and benefits to CA veterans and their families with a vision to insure that CA veterans will live the highest quality of life with dignity and honor. Serving veterans from all branches of the military, CDVA's areas of service include; housing for veterans, Long-term care for veterans, and advocacy services for veterans. www.calvet.ca.gov

State Resources

Troops to Trucks Program: The CA Department of Motor Vehicles announced the availability of this program aimed at streamlining the commercial driver license application process by eliminating the road skills driving test requirement.

A commercial driver license is required in CA to operate large trucks and buses. To obtain a CDL, the applicant must be at least 18 years of age and pass a commercial medical examination, a vision examination, applicable knowledge (written) tests, and the road skills driving test.

Under the Troops to Trucks Program, CDL applicants will not have to take the road skills driving test. Recent state and federal law changes allow the DMV to waive the road skills driving test for qualified military personnel (two or more years of military, heavy truck driving experience) applying for CA CDL. For more details on this program or how to obtain a CDL, visit the CA DMV at www.dmv.ca.gov and search keyword "troops".

Zero8hundred's "Navigators": Is a new effort the help military sailors settle into civilian life in San Diego County. This project has an agreement with the Navy to link up with Sailors before they shed the uniform. All the "navigators" – all interns from the University of Southern California's social work master's program – will track existing sailors starting at six months before discharge and will touch base with these veterans at three-month intervals for a year after discharge.

The point is to put former troops in touch with whatever help might be needed-counseling for PTSD, for example, or emergency financial grants or education advice. They are hoping to expand the program to Marine Corps and Coast Guard sometime soon. For further information go to http://www.zero8hundred.org/

COLORADO:

Challenge Aspen Military Opportunities (CAMO): Provides recreational and cultural experiences for wounded warriors with cognitive or physical disabilities. Provides couples retreats. https://challengeaspen.org/military/

Colorado SBDC: Along with its existing partners, will coordinate a multi-state effort, collaborating with strategic partners to create an integrated one-stop virtual resource for veteran-owned small businesses. This resource will provide information and high quality, cost-effective small business assistance to the veteran community through internet-based counseling, training, social networking and a veteran database registry. http://www.coloradosbdc.org/

Homes for All Veterans: Manages services to promote housing stability and alleviate chronic homelessness. Funded through a grant from the VA. http://denveroptions.atendesigngroup.com/hav

Vet 2 Trucks Program: If you are close to completing your military obligation or were discharged within the last 90 days, this program can put you behind the wheel of a new career. You may be eligible for this program if you drove heavy vehicles during your time in the military. To be qualified, you must: Be currently serving, close to discharge or have been discharged within the last 90 days. Have experience driving heavy military trucks with a safe driving record for the last two years. **Benefits:** Eliminate $200-$400 costs of test/ Eliminate $150 - $250 test vehicle rental expense/Eliminate the $14.00 Learner's Permit Fee. No need to schedule a testing appointment and Quicker entry into the workforce. https://www.colorado.gov/dmv and/or Troops to Truckers http://www.troopstotruckers.com/

State Resources

PROCESS: Complete, sign and date the front page of the Application for Military CDL Skills Test Waiver. Have your Commanding Office complete, sign and date the back of the Military CD< Skills Test Waiver. Complete, sign and date the CO DMV CDL Unit 10 Year History License Certification. Submit the completed forms to the CO DMV Unit either by fax to 303-205-5754 or by mail to: Colorado Division of Motor Vehicles, CDL Unit, Room 154, 1881 Pierce Street, Lakewood, CO 80214.

If you have not already done so, arrange for Department of Transportation (DOT) Medical Examination through your physician or health care facility, and get your DOT Medical.

Pass the written test of the Colorado CDL Manual for General Knowledge, Combination if you want a Class A CDL and air brakes (if applicable).

Once qualified for the waiver, go to Secretary of State Office, take and pass the applicable written tests, tender your DOT Medical card and purchase your CDL. (Rules for proof of identity, legal name, age, lawful, presence and residential address apply as applicable).

Although the program serves as a great benefit to any veterans attempting to become truck drivers in the state of Colorado, it's important to note the time requirement involved. Make sure to maximize your transition by researching whether or not this program is for you, and understanding how long it will take to apply and be processed.

Veteran Green Jobs: Is a non-profit, their mission is to connect military veterans with meaningful employment opportunities that serve our communities and environment. They help vets find career opportunities in stable economic sectors related to energy efficiency and energy conservation; clean and renewable energy; natural resource conservation; environmental restoration; and other sustainability sectors. http://veteransgreenjobs.org/ Site that provides opportunities in this area:
http://www.veteransfirecorps.org/current-opportunities

Welcome Home Montrose (WHM) – Warrior Resource Center: Provides a centralized location to connect wounded warriors, veterans and their families with support, services and social activities in Montrose community. **Voice program:** Offers wounded warriors, veterans and service members the opportunity to record their story using Dragon software, a dictation/transcription program. They can add images to their story and chose to keep it private or share it. **Dream Job Program:** Invites wounded warriors to live in Montrose, CO for six months as they try out their dream job with a personal mentor. They will also serve as consultants to WHM, identifying gaps in community services for veterans and wounded warriors. http://welcomehomemontrose.org/

CONNECTICUT:

Veterans Network Directory: List of a variety of veteran resources. http://veteransnetwork.net/directory.php

Veterans Non-Profits and Charities: Offers a list of a variety of state resources and their ratings. http://greatnonprofits.org/categories/view/veterans

Mindful Yoga Therapy: Helping veterans and their families to find a calm and steady body/mind to continue productive and peaceful lives through the support of the mindful practices of yoga. Their programs are clinically tested. They have been working with veterans with Post Traumatic Stress Disorder (PTSD) in residential treatment programs and in outpatient programs for several years...... This work led to the development of Mindful Yoga Therapy. http://mindfulyogatherapy.org/wp/about-yoga-for-veterans/mindful-yoga-therapy/

Mindful Yoga Therapy is shared by:

- developing personalized programs for the individual needs of the veteran

State Resources

231

- offering discounts and scholarships to veterans and their families for classes and programs in affiliate studios
- offering partial scholarships to our Yoga Teacher Training Programs
- teaching Mindful Yoga Therapy in therapeutic treatment settings
- teaching Mindful Yoga Therapy at veterans Centers at Universities
- training yoga teachers and yoga therapists to use this program and to bring it into treatment centers

DELAWARE:

State Directory Website for Delaware Paralyzed Veterans: Mission is to change lives and build brighter futures for our seriously injured heroes—to empower these brave men and women with what they need to achieve the things they fought for: freedom and independence. http://www.pva.org/

Delaware Joining Forces: Delaware Joining Forces is a state-wide public and private organizational network that guides policy and provides services through its partners to the State's military and veteran communities. No single organization can meet all the needs of our Service Members Veterans and their Families (SMVF), but a community of partners can provide an array of essential services. It also provides a network for referrals and a process for collaboration between service organizations. http://www.delaware.gov/vsd/

Home of the Brave: The first shelter for homeless female veterans and their children in Milford, Delaware. http://www. delawareonline.com/story/news/local/2014/03/28/home-brave-opens-shelter-female-veterans/7040043/

FLORIDA:

K9 Warriors: Is dedicated to providing service canines to warriors suffering from PTSD/traumatic Brain Injury as a result of military service Post 9/11. Our goal is to give a new leash on life to rescue dogs and military heroes, empowering warriors to return to civilian life with dignity and independence.
http://www.k9sforwarriors.org **A fan and personal favorite!!**

Veterans Ocean Adventure (VOA): Mission is to create an opportunity for veterans to experience the healing power of water. They create an opportunity for disabled veterans to experience open ocean sailing. VOA provides offshore cruising and scuba diving through collaboration with community partners including the Miami VA and Miami Vet Center. Once participants have completed the introduction to Water Sports Program and expressed a desire to advance to blue water sailing. Veterans Ocean Adventures provides an introduction to cruising in the Florida Keys and the Bahamas. Select participants may continue on to join a leg of an ongoing world circumnavigation. http://veteransoceanadventures.org **This is a awesome organization; I am a fan of healing through water therapy...for me it brings peace.**

GEORIGA:

Hopes and Dreams Riding Facility: This is a great place for the service members to go and relax, use the lodge, enjoy the festivities and camp...and with their family. Go for a horse ride around their place, bond with a horse, or schedule a trail ride through the wilderness and enjoy nature. Their staff provides counselors if service members or their family need someone to talk to. Horses are a proven way of therapy, both physically and mentally. Services are provided to wounded warriors, veterans, active duty and their loved ones. Also their doors are open to love ones who served but did not come home.
http://hopesanddreamsridingfacility.com **A personal favorite; equine therapy is very healing.**

Ketia4Kids: Adrian & Corena Swanier Scholarship recognized the contributions and provides educational assistance for our military children. The program awards five $1,000 scholarships for use towards a four-year degree, vocational or technical certificate. Only dependent unmarried children under 21 (23 if enrolled as a full-time student) of active duty personnel, retired military members, or survivors of deceased members, may apply for a scholarship. http://ketia4kidz.org

Fisher House Comfort Homes: Provides FREE temporary housing for families of patients receiving medical care at major military and VA medical centers. http://www.tampa.va.gov/services/Fisher_House.asp

ServiceSource-Warrior Bridge in Florida: Provides employment services including assistance with resume writing, interviewing skills, identifying appropriate job openings and removing barriers related to transportation and training for veterans with disabilities. www.servicesource.org/warrior-bridge

HAWAII:

American Red Cross – Hawaii: Offices throughout the state provides assistance to the Armed Forces, Red Cross Clubs, First Aid Station Teams (FAST) and disaster preparedness. http://www.redcross.org/hi/honolulu

Employer Support of the Guard & Reserve (ESGR): List of ESGR Committee contacts. Each committee has trained volunteer ombudsmen who help resolve issues between employers and their employees who serve in the National Guard and Reserve. Services may include Uniformed Services Employment and Re-employment Rights Act (USERRA) information, informal mediation and referral services to resolve conflicts. http://www.esgr.mil/contact/local-state-pages/hawaii.aspx
**I highly respect this organization They work hard to keep companies in check and honoring our service member's rights

and the laws of our country. ESGR took on UPS years ago when they tried to fire my husband because he was Army National Guard and activated. Thankfully they saved my husband's job and he never had problems with UPS again.

IDAHO:

Caregiver Resources: Provides an amazing listing of caregiver resources for this state and others. http://www.fiaboise.org/caregiver-resources

Resource Veteran Network Community Guide: This guide has pages full of resources with point of contact information. https://police.cityofboise.org/media/487172/veteransresource_manual_8-23-13.pdf

Veteran Network.org: The mission of the Idaho Veterans Network is to help distressed veterans and their families by facilitating peer-to-peer support and guiding them to resources available to them in order to create a veteran population that is capable, confident, and committed to their community. http://www.idahoveteransnetwork.org/

ILLINOIS:

Giant City State Park's Equine Therapy Program: The Illinois Department of Natural Resources (IDNR): Is launching a two-year pilot project with the Veterans Affairs Medical Center in Marion, Illinois to offer equine therapy for armed forces veterans at Giant City State Park in Makanda. The medical center will refer, as appropriate, veterans living with PTSD or other mental health issues to the Equine Therapy Program. More than 25 horses, ponies and mules, will participate in the pilot project, which began on January 1, 2015. www.SESTherapeuticRiding.com

State Resources

Joining Forces: Provides a directory of networked military and veteran resources in Illinois, personal assistance and a calendar of veteran and military events. Users can also browse by category or full directory.
http://illinoisjoiningforces.org

Veterans Assistance Commission of McHenry County: provides services to veterans in financial assistance, VA claims and advocacy, transportation to the Captain James A. Lovell Federal Health Care Center and referrals assistance.
http://www.illinoisjoiningforces.org

Veteran Legal Support Center & Clinic: Specializes in appealing denied veterans' benefits claims, including service-connected benefits, pension benefits, survivor benefits and educational benefits. VLSC will not begin work on an initial claim that has not been filed or is currently pending before the VA. http://www.jmls.edu/

INDIANA:

Horticultural Healing: Veterans will have the opportunity to grow their own food through a new horticultural healing program starting in Ft. Wayne, Indiana. Sponsored by Greenleaf, Urban Gardening and Horticultural Healing, the program will give clients hands on vocational training that combines rehabilitation, healing and allows clients to create a food garden. The idea is to help veterans who are challenged by physical and emotional challenges such as PTSD. Class size will be 15 clients a year and program members will attend four hours a week for 36 weeks. There is a $200 program fee. For more information,
EMAIL: pollinatingpeace@gmail.com
http://wboi.org/term/horticultural-healing

Hoosier Veterans Assistance Program: Provides housing and reintegration services to veterans experiencing homelessness;

and administer programs to prevent at risk veterans from becoming homeless. http://www.hvafofindiana.org/

IOWA:

Home Base Iowa: Is a new program that allows Iowa businesses and military people to come together for employment opportunities. The program helps veterans find jobs, explore career paths and make a smooth transition to civilian life in Iowa. The program's website features job postings, links to job fairs, and up-to-date information about educational opportunities, National Guard recruiting, job training and much more. For more information, go to www.homebaseiowa.org or call (855) 942-4692.

Iowa Aid & Assistance Programs: A great resource site loaded with resources for various needs for our military community. http://www.needhelppayingbills.com/html/iowa_assistance_programs.html

Iowa - My ArmyBenefits.org: http://myarmybenefits.us.army.mil/Home.html

Iowa Farmer Veteran Resource Guide: If you're a veteran or service member looking to build your farm business, the Farmer Veteran Coalition of Iowa has tools to help lay a strong foundation. Start with the Farm Building Resource Guide for information on critical issues for a successful farm business. Next, utilize our network of service provides and other farmers that can provide further advice on constructing your farm business. http://iowafarmerveteran.org/

KANSAS:

Kansas Legal Services: Nonprofit Law Firm and Community Education Organization. http://www.kansaslegalservices.org/

State Resources

Student Veteran Virtual Resource Center:
http://www.umkc.edu/veterans/

Veteran Owned Businesses: This site offers an amazing lists of veteran owned businesses and resources for the state of Kansas. http://www.veteranownedbusiness.com/

KENTUCKY:

Fellednot.com: The VET2VET program realizes there are numerous resources available through the VA and other government entities, but they feel the system is overcrowded and often, veterans wait weeks for an appointment. This program meets veterans daily who either need someone to talk to about their struggles, or who want to do something to help those younger veterans now coming home from battle with "Invisible Wounds of War." Those who mentor say it helps them in their own healing to reach out and help someone else who is. The program also offers Veterans an opportunity to give and receive help within the veteran community. If you are a veteran struggling with PTSD or TBI and would like and would like to talk to other veterans who have moved further along in the journey with overcoming the "Invisible Wounds of War." For more information contact support@fellednot.com. http://fellednot.com/vet2vet/ **New resource for me but I really like their points and plan of assistance. I look forward to hearing more from this group.**

VET2VET FAMILIES: Family members struggle when their loved ones return from war with PTSD and TBI. In fact, it is very likely that the family members will develop Secondary Traumatic Stress Syndrome (STSD). Because the world of Invisible Wounds is so difficult to endure for the affected individual, the family often bears the brunt of the veteran's problem. Families want to help their loved one, but most do not understand the reality of surviving a war zone and can often make the problems worse due to a lack of understanding and a desperate need to want to make things better for the PTSD survivor. This program gives family members of veterans a chance to find support within the local community. Whether you are the spouse, the child, the parent, the sibling, or the friend of one who suffers with PTSD or TBI, you need a support system for yourself. This organization was started for the very reason that we, as family members of one who has been diagnosed with PTSD and TBI, have walked a long and difficult path, without any support. The military, nor our government, are able to handle the magnitude of this problem. For those of us out in the civilian world that must be a strong support to our wounded warriors, we need to encourage one another and help to keep our families strong. PTSD and TBI destroy relationships, families, and lives.

If you are struggling with these issues, then you have the experience needed to make the VET2VET FAMILIES program a success. By sharing, you will help others move forward and you will help yourself at the same time. For more information contact support@fellednot.com. http://fellednot.com/vet2vet/ **I really like this organization, fan favorite!**

The Kentucky SBDC: Created by vetbiz.com to provide veterans with information about the services available through the Kentucky SBDC and other organizations that assist veterans. The portal provides on-line business courses in English and in Spanish, lists events and workshops occurring statewide, have a blog on popular topics for veteran business owners, and links federal, state and local resources available to veterans. The Kentucky SBDC is also active in veteran's transition events. http://ksbdc.org/

LOUISIANA:

Louisiana Veterans Foundation: Cares about the welfare of those who have and continue to serve our military. Their goal is to assist Veterans, their families, and the families of active duty military personnel that reside in the state of Louisiana who

State Resources

have a qualified need that cannot be met through their own resources or other community resources. http://lavetsfest.org/

National Guard Resource Directory: http://geauxguard.com/ resources/national-resource-directory/

MAINE:

The Maine SBDC: Provides a technology-based programs to provide the military business community with the tools to overcome the barriers to entrepreneurship. The project will include a marketing initiative to promote the educational services of the Maine SBDC available to the veteran community, provide online counseling and distance learning, and create a veterans assistance portal by coordinating with other organizations that assist veterans. http://www.mainesbdc.org/

Easter Seals of Maine: Easter Seals Maine's Military & Veterans services is working hard to fill these gaps in services. They offer military and veterans systems of care with viable options to support and augment current reintegration efforts. Their mission is to provide critical and timely financial assistance when no other resource is available to veterans, service members and their families, to ensure their dignity, health and overall well-being. http://www.easterseals.com/maine/our-programs/military-veteran-services/

Homeless Veterans Alliance: The Maine Homeless Veterans Alliance, a 501c3 non-profit organization, provides assistance and resources to homeless and otherwise needy veterans of the United States armed forces, with a focus on Southern Maine, as well as to educate the public about their needs and contributions of them and those of their families. Running strictly off donations, the MHVA hopes to expand to reach more Maine veterans and eventually establish a shelter. https://www.facebook.com/MaineHomelessVeteransAlliance

MARYLAND:

Fisher House Comfort Homes – Walter Reed National Military Medical Center at Bethesda I, II, III, IV, V: Provides FREE temporary housing for families of patients receiving medical care at major military and VA medical centers in the Washington DC area. http://www.wrnmmc.capmed.mil/SitePages/home.aspx

Coalition of Families for Children's Mental Health – Military Families: Supports service members, veterans and their children with mental health and behavioral conditions in the Fort Meade area. http://www.mdcoalition.org/services/military-families

USO-Metro: Is a non-profit chartered by Congress and dedicated to "serving those who serve, and their families" in Washington D.C., Maryland and N. Virginia. It is through the generous financial support of individuals and organizations in the local community that USO-Metro is able to full its mission. With the help of thousands of devoted volunteers, USO-Metro provides programs and services for active duty troops and their families at area military hospitals, six USO Centers, four USO airport lounges and Mobile USO. Signature programs and services include holiday programs like Turkeys for Troops and Project USO Elf, emergency housing and food assistance, and caring for our wounded, ill and injured troops and their caregivers. www.us.uso.org/washingtonbaltimore/ ** **I Love the USO, such a great group of friendly and caring volunteers!!**

MASSACHUSETTS:

MA – Benefits for Dependents of a Veteran: Presents information about state-level veterans' benefits available to dependents. http://www.mass.gov/veterans/

MA – Department of Veterans' Services – Women Veterans' Network: Offers a central resource for women veterans in MA through the Women Veteran Network of the DVS. www.mass.gov/veterans/women-veterans/

MA Treasury – Veterans' Bonus Division: Pays bonuses to qualified veterans, service members and their families for service in the US Military. www.mass.gov/treasury/veterans

MA Dept. of Veteran Services – Statewide Housing Advocacy Reintegration and Prevention (S.H.A.R.P): Emergency shelter at a veteran-centric facility. www.mass.gov/veterans/housing/sharp.html

MA – Vehicle Adaptations for Disabled Veterans: Offers assistance and much more. www.mass.gov/portal

MICHIGAN: See separate chapter

MINNESOTA:

Brooklyn Park Beyond the Yellow Ribbon Network: Connects service members and their families with community support, training, services and resources in and around Brooklyn Park, this is part of the MN Yellow Ribbon Program. www.beyondtheyellowribbon.org

First City Yellow Ribbon Network: Works closely with the Beltrami County Service Office and local veteran organizations to ensure they are able to reach every veteran. Host of the "Project New Hope" Veteran's Retreat. www.Firstcityyellowribbonnetwork.weebly.com

Lower St. Croix Valley Network: Supports communities, service members, veterans and military families through special events and workshops including: Lumberjack days, the Bayport

Memorial Day Parade and Lake St. Croix Beach Heritage Days. www.beyondtheyellowribbon.org/lake-st-croix-beach

MISSISSIPPI:

Crusaders for Veterans: Reaches out to provide the care and respect that our veterans (all branches and eras) deserve. Programs provided are support, counseling, resources, emergency funds and housing. Questions Email: cfv@crusadersforveterans.net
http://crusadersforveterans.net/

Military One-Click-Mississippi: Provides a variety of veteran resources for their military community. http://militaryoneclick.com/veterans/

MISSOURI:

Camp Hope: provides outdoor adventures to combat wounded veterans of the global war on terrorism and active duty combat-wounded soldiers, marines, airmen and sailors. No Cost to veterans and can accommodate up to 6 veterans per week. www.chrisnealfarm.com

U.S. VETS – St. Louis: Provides transitional housing, case management, employment assistance, job training, and career planning to homeless veterans. http://www.usvetsinc.org/st-louis

MONTANA:

Grateful Nation: A nonprofit organization located in Missoula, MT, the headquarters hometown of ALPS Corp. Grateful Nation was formed for the specific purpose of facilitating college educations for the children of soldiers killed while on active duty in Iraq or Afghanistan. The organization currently focuses solely on providing these resources and support to Montana military families. Grateful Nation, Montana also partners with a national high-end apparel maker Spyder and outdoor retailers Bob Ward and Sons in Missoula and Scheels All Sports in Great Falls to offer a limited release tactical sweater jacket, with 100 percent of profits going to support the organization's mission." http://www.gratefulnationmontana.com/

Montana Veterans Foundation: A non-profit organization is designed to assist homeless veterans (or veterans at risk of homelessness) by improving their quality of life and providing comprehensive support which enables veterans to achieve greater self-sufficiency. http://www.mtvf.org/

Volunteers of America – Northern Rockies – Homeless Veterans Reintegration Program: Offers services to assist in reintegrating homeless veterans to meaningful employment www.voanr.org/services/veteranservices/HVRP

NEBRASKA:

The Nebraska SBDC: Will provide services to veterans by coordinating with the veterans Administration, the Nebraska Department of Labor, the veterans in Business Forum, the Nebraska National Guard, and the 55th Air Wing and Strategic Air Command at Offutt Air Force Base. It will use new media and speeches to service clubs and other organizations to reach veterans, particularly at the early stages. The center will develop a Web site for veterans to serve as a portal to online counseling and courses, and provide sound and timely information on starting and running a business. http://nbdc.unomaha.edu/

Nebraska Veterans Leader Corps (NVLC): The Veteran Leader Corps Program and its three full-time AmeriCorps members works to ensure a successful transition back into civilian life for returning veterans by providing job training and readiness resources, information and help navigating veterans benefits, community engagement and networking opportunities and referral services to their mental health and education partners if deemed necessary.

NVLC focus on connecting veterans with local resources and community opportunities when they transition home from military service. NCR's veteran services come at an important time when veterans return home to Nebraska communities. They continue to provide job readiness and training services, job development resources for employers and community engagement and networking opportunities for returning veterans and members of the community.

For job readiness and training services, contact Cliff McEvoy at cliffmcevoy@nereform.org, For community engagement services and opportunities, contact Rachel Gehringer-Wiar at rachegw@nereform.org, For job development resources for employers contact Sara Tangdall at Sara.tangdall@nereform.org

Update: The NVLC community employment Guide with Nebraska specific job readiness resources is available from their website.
http://nereform.org/nebraska-veteran-leader-corps

NEVADA:

Adopt-a-Vet Dental Program: Offers FREE dental care to Northern Nevada's low-income veterans who are in critical need. Services provided include treatment for oral decay, abscesses and infections. http://www.adoptavetdental.com/

Veterans Resource Guide: 8 News NOW and their Community Pride Partners, NV Energy, Findlay Automotive Group, Greenman, Goldberg, Raby and Martinez Law Firm and Greater Las Vegas Association of Realtors proudly support the brave men and women in their community that have served in our military and gave so much to our country. This list provides a numerous amount of resources in their community to assist veterans with government assistance, employment, health care, housing/financial aid, and education. http://www.8newsnow.com/story/23292565/las-vegas-veterans-resource-guide

NEW HAMPSHIRE:

Friends of Veterans: The Friends of Veterans (FOV) is a public non-profit (501(C)3) organization who relies on grants, tax deductible donations, and a variety of fundraisers to support our efforts. Their Board Members and staff are 100% volunteer, which means, 100% of the funds received are used towards their efforts to end the homelessness amongst our veterans. Go to their website to review programs provided at http://www.friendsofveteransvtnh.org/

New Hampshire Assistance & Programs: Find aid, help, grants, and locate assistance programs in all cities and counties in New Hampshire, including Nashua and Manchester; to include all areas of a veteran and their family's needs. http://www.needhelppayingbills.com/html/new_hampshire_assistance_progr.html

NEW JERSEY:

Easter Seals – New Jersey: Easter Seals' newly added Military & Veterans services respond to this call to action. As the largest provider of disability-related services to individuals with disabilities and their families, Easter Seals offers military and veterans systems of care with viable options to support and augment current reintegration efforts for veterans in communities across our nation.

Easter Seals New Jersey is currently working diligently with local organizations to construct program offerings that work to fill the gaps of service for veterans and existing service members in our great state. To find out what we have in the works or to ensure notification when our programs launch, please contact Chief Programs Officer, Shelley Samuels at ssamuels@nj.easterseals.com their website is http://www.easterseals.com/nj/our-programs/military-veteran-services/

Real Warriors, Real Battles, Real Strength: Organizations offering specialized programs and resources to service members, their families and their health care providers on a state or local level. These organizations may be affiliates of national organizations as well, but have programming specific to a smaller geographic area.
http://www.realwarriors.net/partner/local.php

Welcome Home Veterans: Is composed of family members, friends, coworkers, civic organizations and businesses, all supporting our soldiers and their families. Most of our members are veterans themselves or of the generation that lived through the Vietnam conflict. Many veterans were not received home with the respect they earned, nor were they cared for properly upon their return. Homelessness, unemployment and lack of specialized medical care are among the problems we help our vets overcome.

An important part of our mission is to solicit, engage and network to identify veterans who are in need, not all of whom are obvious and not all of whom readily come forward. Our goal is simple: Take care of our military families; our soldiers and veterans in need from ALL branches and eras of time served.
http://www.welcomehomevetsofnj.org/

State Resources

NEW YORK:

Experience Counts: Is geared to help veterans and support their transition into the civilian work force. Although the scope of the program is somewhat restricted, the opportunities it can offer outweigh the lack of diversity. Veterans can use the program to become licensed armed security guards through on-site training and are relatively guaranteed to find related jobs.
http://www.ny.gov/ click on "veterans initiative"

Troops to Teachers: Centralized information and resources location to help veterans and service members become public school teachers in New York.
http://troopstoteachers.net

The N.Y. State SBDC: Created a special "Veterans Business Services" (www.nyssbdc.org/services/veterans/veterans.html) that links available services to veterans in the state and also to federal, state and local resources. Online training and business development are also available from the site. The program director participates in seminars for veterans throughout the state and plans events tailored to veterans.
http://www.nyssbdc.org/

Unified Behavioral Health Center: Offers a centralized location for service members, veterans and their families to receive mental health care at no cost.
www.northport.va.gov

Zion House: Offers female veterans safe and supportive housing where they have the opportunity to locate and procure permanent housing, financial security, as well as educational and vocational opportunities.
http://zionhouseavon.org

If the training isn't completed through a state Career Center, veterans may utilize schools or an employer at a cost. Once a veteran has completed their training, Career Center staff will connect them with one of the 8,000+ security jobs available within New York. For more information, check out the veteran section at http://www.labor.ny.gov/vets/vetintropage.shtm.

NORTH CAROLINA:

American Hero Shuttle: Offers low rates for a daily shuttle service for veterans to the W.G. (Bill) Hefner VA Medical Center in Salisbury and Charlotte Community Based Outpatient Clinic.
http://www.manta.com/c/mb4npjt/american-hero-shuttle-llc

Charlotte VA Community Based Outpatient Clinic (CBOC): Offers various healthcare services for veterans in the Charlotte metropolitan area. www.hnfs.com

Hickory VA Community Based Outpatient Clinic: Offers various healthcare services for veterans in the Hickory area.

Winston-Salem VA Community Based Outpatient Clinic: Offers various healthcare services for veterans in the Winston-Salem metropolitan area.

United Service Organization (USO): Provides support services, recreation activities and volunteer opportunities for service members and military families. www.uso-nc.org.

NORTH DAKOTA:

Military Ovation: Supports veterans and their families through employment, education, training and support groups www.nd.gov

State Resources

Professional Veterans Advocates of North Dakota: The Professional Veterans Advocates of North Dakota (PVAND) is an organization of County Veterans Service Officers and associates who are dedicated to improving the lives of veterans of the U.S. Armed Forces, and their families. We assist our clients to obtain benefits from the U.S. Department of Veterans Affairs (VA), the State of North Dakota, and other agencies. We are united for the following purposes:

* Provide training and education to County VSOs and their staff members * Promote the welfare and rights of veterans statewide through legislative initiatives * Provide members with a collaborative network of resources, information, and ideas and * Develop innovative approaches to training and advocacy. http://www.pvand.net/

NEW MEXICO:

New Mexico Direct Caregivers Coalition: Trains, educates and advocates for caregivers across New Mexico. http://www.nmdcc.org

Veterans Fire Corps (Part of Veterans Green Job): CURRENT OPPORTUNITIES: All programs are operated in partnership with local conservation corps and Veterans Green Jobs. There are currently three corps, the California Conservation Corps (CA only), Southwest Conservation Corps (CO, NM), Arizona Conservation Corps (AZ, NM) and the Student Conservation Association (nationwide) that are running Veterans Fire Corps programs.

Please contact these programs directly for additional information about specific program opportunities. VFC programs operate in Arizona, California, Colorado, New Mexico, and Arizona during the winter, spring, summer and fall season. For additional details and specific information, click on the links below that will take you to individual websites for each corps.

For more information on programs in Colorado and Northern New Mexico, in partnership with the Southwest Conservation Corps, http://www.sccorps.org/join/veteran-fire-corps/

For more information on programs in Arizona and Southern New Mexico, in partnership with the Arizona Conservation Corps, http://www.azcorps.org/join/

OHIO:

Legal Aid Society of Columbus: Supplies pro bono legal aid to veterans, service members and their families including VA and state benefits, discharge status upgrades, homeless at risk assistance, and other civil legal issues. www.columbuslegalaid.org

New Educational Transfer Credit Law: A new law encourages veterans to get their college degree by offering college credit for training received during their time in the military. The bill creates the Military Transfer Assurance Guide to provide a business of standards, procedures and tools for granting college credit for military experience for any public college and university, providing more consistent services across the state system. Higher education institutions must provide these college credits for FREE. Also, priority registration will be granted to veterans to make sure they receive the necessary classes to earn a degree. For more information, call the Ohio Department of Veteran Services at (616) 644-0898 or contact your county service officer.

OKLAHOMA:

Jack C. Montgomery VA Medical Center – Adaptive Sports Program: Offer opportunities to disabled veterans to become involved in adaptive sports, outdoor recreation,

State Resources

fitness programs and leisure activities. This facility also offers various programs for veterans in others areas, including homeless veterans. www.muskogee.va.gov.

The Oklahoma SBDC: Located in a state with four active installations that strive to work closely with each installation to provide services to veterans and military personnel. They will also work closely with Army family readiness groups and provide training and education to veterans, and their families, who are in business or are considering starting a business. The center will provide resources to military personnel that will transition to the civilian world. The SBDC will also offer training sessions and workshops via live video feed through a distance learning center, and expand on established channels of communication to reach veterans in need of assistance. http://www.oksbdc.org/

OREGON:

Forest Grove Fire & Rescue: Is the first Fire Department in the state that has had its student-volunteer program approved as an official On-The-Job (OTJ) training program, which means the VA can now pay veterans serving as student-volunteer firefighters (formerly "interns") in the same way it pays apprentices in other fields.

A firefighting career has been a logical landing spot for former service members, as the profession requires teamwork, camaraderie, and being able to keep your head in dangerous and life-threatening situations. The Forest Grove program may open the doors for other firefighting programs to join OTJ. http://jobsforveterans.military.com/1469/fighting-fire-opening-vet-jobs/

The Oregon SBDC: Has provided a customized Veterans Small Business Management Program engaging National Guard business owners affected by unexpected by deployment and difficult economic times. The training will allow peer veteran sharing of information and best practices in business while developing strategic planning solutions to help Oregon's veterans. The center will serve as a one-stop point of contact and deliver services through traditional one-on-one counseling and simultaneous distance education, VoIP audio and Web technology to eliminate time and distance barriers.http://www.bizcenter.org/

Oregon Veteran Foundation: Offers a central location for several groups to combine resources, optimizing public and private dollars to care for veterans. http://oregonveteransfoundation.org

Returning Veterans Project: Connects Veterans, service members and their families with volunteer providers in Oregon and Southwest Washington offering counseling and health care treatment to deal with all phases of a deployment. http://www.returningveterans.org/

PENNSYLVANIA:

Vets Journey Home (VJH): Is an all-volunteer organization that helps with the emotional healing of service members. VJH started in 1989 as Bamboo Bridge to work on the emotional healing of Viet Nam Vets. In 2004 the name was changed to include all active duty, reserve and veterans, all service times and all branches of service. All retreats are FREE to service members. They are located in Wisconsin, Maryland, Pennsylvania, Florida, Texas and California. The volunteers are veterans and civilian family members of vets, reserves, or active duty. The weekend retreats are put on to assist participants with unloading the emotional baggage they carry due to experiences in service to our country. www.vetsjourneyhome.org ****I really like this organization and the work/assistance they offer. Definite fan favorite!**

State Resources

Vet Entrepreneur Program in Philly: St. Joseph's University in Philadelphia, PA is launching a program to provide disabled veterans with education and resources to start their own business. The program will be overseen by the newly formed Office of Veterans Services and provided at no cost to eligible participants.

The intensive, three-part program provides an eight-week online course to provide veterans with foundation in business fundamentals and guidance in developing a business plan. The second phase is a seven-day residency and the third part of the program is a six month mentorship, with access to complimentary support services. www.sju.edu/vej

RHODE ISLAND:

Division of Veterans Affairs-Human Resources: Links to resources for assisting homeless veterans, HUD questions and Stand Down Events.
http://www.vets.ri.gov/housing/homeless/index.php

The Point: R.I. Resource Guide for their community with Disabilities and Veterans.
http://adrc.ohhs.ri.gov/assistance/help_for_veterans.php

SOUTH CAROLINA:

South Carolina Military Family Fund (SCMFRF): Provides monetary grants to families of South Carolina National Guard members and South Carolina residents serving in the U.S. Armed Forces Reserve components who were called to active duty as a result of the September 11, 2001 terrorist attacks. www.checkoff.sc.gov

Veteran Owned Businesses for S.C.: Provides links and resources for non-profits, veteran and other useful information. http://www.veteranownedbusiness.com/172/nonprofit-and-free-help

SCIWAY (South Carolina's Information Highway): Provides links, point of contact information and websites by each county in the state.
http://www.sciway.net/org/community/richland.html

SOUTH DAKOTA:

Veterans Fire Corps (Part of Veterans Green Job): CURRENT OPPORTUNITIES: All programs are operated in partnership with local conservation corps and Veterans Green Jobs. There are currently three corps, the California Conservation Corps (CA only), Southwest Conservation Corps (CO, NM), Arizona Conservation Corps (AZ, NM) and the Student Conservation Association (nationwide) that are running Veterans Fire Corps programs.

Please contact these programs directly for additional information about specific program opportunities. VFC programs operate in Arizona, California, Colorado, New Mexico, and Arizona during the winter, spring, summer and fall season. For additional details and specific information, click on the links below that will take you to individual websites for each corps.

For more information on programs in Arizona and South Dakota, in partnership with the Student Conservation Association, http://www.thesca.org/

VFW POST 3179 Pheasant Hunts: This Post in Faulkton, S.D. sponsors pheasant hunts for seriously wounded vets. Services are free or at-cost. VFW's Military Assistance Program covers airfare, as well as hunting licenses. To qualify, a veteran must have enough upper body strength to weild a shotgun, but confinement to a wheelchair is not an obstacle. Amputees are encouraged to apply for the trip. Applicants must possess

State Resources

a Purple Heart. Submit a copy of your DD-214 as well as VA disability rating documentation, personal contract information, war zone dates, unit and details of your wounds to the post. **This is very cool; it is awesome to see an organization and members reach out and assist our wounded warriors in this capacity. This is very compassionate! Fan Favorite!**

TEXAS:

The San Antonio SBDC: Has created a new website to be a one-stop reference for veterans and military personnel who are new entrepreneurs or small business owners. It provides self-assessment tools, on-line counseling, distance learning, web-based assessments, government contracting assistance, business planning and start-up assistance and help with preparation of applications for bank loans and financing. The web site connects the resources of federal, state, and local entities that are available to veterans. http://sasbdc.org/

TexVet: Supports Texas military, veterans and family members with information and referral services and by facilitating the delivery of those services across traditional boundaries. TexVet is dedicated to providing veterans, military members and their families with equal access to information. By collecting federal, state and local Veteran Service Organization (VSO) information. TexVet has created an online Veteran Services Provider Network (VSPN).

Through this network and event based activities TexVet has initiated a "No Wrong Door" policy for the veteran community. Their partners across Texas have become more knowledgeable about the other services available to veterans. In turn, veterans are properly connected to the services they need and request. http://www.texvet.org/

Vet Business Start-Up Support in Austin: The Bunker Austin, a program geared to help veterans become entrepreneurs, has launched at the University of Texas at Austin. The program is going to be a one-stop place for Texas veterans to plug into all the resources available in Austin. Other cities with similar "Bunker" programs include Chicago, Los Angeles, Tacoma, Colorado Springs, Kansas City, Washington D.C. and Philadelphia. At Bunker Austin, veteran-led startups will have access to mentorship, a network of veteran entrepreneurs and help find venture capital. www.thebunkeraustin.com

Vets Journey Home (VJH): Is an all-volunteer organization that helps with the emotional healing of service members. VJH started in 1989 as Bamboo Bridge to work on the emotional healing of Viet Nam Vets. In 2004 the name was changed to include all active duty, reserve and veterans, all service times and all branches of service. All retreats are FREE to service members. They are located in Wisconsin, Maryland, Pennsylvania, Florida, Texas and California. The volunteers are veterans and civilian family members of vets, reserves, or active duty. The weekend retreats are put on to assist participants with unloading the emotional baggage they carry due to experiences in service to our country. www.vetsjourneyhome.org

TENNESSEE:

Fisher House Comfort Homes: Provides FREE temporary housing for families of patients receiving medical care at major military and VA medical centers in the Tennessee area. http://www.tennesseefisherhouse.org/

Nia Association: Supports active-duty service members and families who register with the Ft. Campbell Exceptional Family Member Program (EFMP) in various areas....such as deployment, emotional, substance, medical and personal. This is a mandatory enrollment program and works with various military & civilian agencies to provide comprehensive coordinated community support; housing, educational, medical and personal services to families with special needs. This includes a two week (FREE) summer camp

State Resources

for children over the age of 3 whose family is in enrolled in EFMP. www.campbell.army.mil/services/crisis/pages/exceptionalfamilymembers.aspx

UTAH:

Utah Veterans Cemetery & Memorial Park: Offers Utah veterans' information on the state operated cemetery, including how to make arrangements to be buried there. http://www.utah.com/

Utah Veterans Home – Southern Utah: Provides residential, nursing and rehabilitive care for elderly and chronically ill veterans and eligible family members. www.Veterans.utah.gov/southern-utah-veterans-home/

Utah Veterans Home – Central Utah: provides residential, nursing and rehabilitive care for elderly and chronically ill veterans and eligible family members. www.Veterans.utah.gov/central-utah-veterans-home/

VERMONT:

Rebuilding Together: Our mission is to work in partnership with the community to rehabilitate the homes of Vermonters of limited means so that they can live in warmth, safety, and independence. Rebuilding Together is a national volunteer organization that works to assure that low-income homeowners, particularly those who are elderly, disabled and wounded veterans, or part of a family with children, live in warmth, safety, and independence. Volunteers descend on homes to paint, clean, fix leaking roofs, replace rotten steps, and do numerous other jobs that make those homes safe and secure. With the support of local companies in the area, Rebuilding Together volunteers transform these homes in a single day, and have a tremendous impact in our community. http://www.rebuildingtogetherburlington.org/

Vermont Outreach Resource Guide – Resources for Service Members & Their Families: Provides a comprehensive directory of resources for military and family members. Includes the VA, National center for PTSD, education, VA Benefits, Veteran's organizations, civilian resources directory and more. http://s3.amazonaws.com/castleton/files/resources/veterans-outreach-guide.pdf

Veterans Service Directory: Useful information for starting and maintaining a business.
http://veterans.vermont.gov/transitions/business

VIRGINIA:

State Employment for Veterans: Provides Veterans access to information about available services and assistance related to employment in Virginia.
http://jobs.virginia.gov/emplforveterans.htm

Department of Juvenile Justice – Veteran Employment Opportunities: Recruits veterans with security related backgrounds for Juvenile Correctional Officer positions and other employment opportunities. http://www.djj.virginia.gov/

USO-Metro: Is a non-profit chartered by Congress and dedicated to "serving those who serve, and their families" in Washington D.C., Maryland and N. Virginia. It is through the generous financial support of individuals and organizations in the local community that USO-Metro is able to full its mission. With the help of thousands of devoted volunteers, USO-Metro provides programs and services for active duty troops and their families at area military hospitals, six USO Centers, four USO airport lounges and Mobile USO. Signature programs and services include holiday programs like Turkeys for Troops and Project USO Elf, emergency housing and food assistance, and caring for our wounded, ill and injured troops and their caregivers. http://us.uso.org/washingtonbaltimore/

State Resources

259

The Virginia SBDC: Provides easy access video guides for veteran owners and prospective business owners covering a wide range of subjects, such as transitioning from the military to business, preparing for deployment, financing and contracting opportunities. The site links vets and reservists to other federal state, and local resources available to veterans. The Virginia SBDC also participates in veteran's conferences and events.http://www.virginiasbdc. org/ and/or www.vetbizresourcecenter.com

Virginia War Memorial - Virginia Heroes: Presents a searchable database including all of Virginia's Heroes who made the ultimate sacrifice from WWII, Korea, Vietnam and Persian Gulf. http://www.vawarmemorial.org

WASHINTON D.C.:

The Commit Foundation: Guides transitioning service members and veterans through mentorships, corporate education and one-on-one transitioning assistance. www.commitfoundation.org

Fallen Heroes Project: The Michael Reagan's Foundation has been producing portraits of Americans killed Afghanistan and Iraq for over 10+ years. He has created over 3,000 beautiful hand drawn renditions of service members killed to present to their families. All of his artwork is provided free-of-charge. His generosity has extended to our allies in Canada and Great Britain. Besides being an internationally recognized artist, Reagan is a Vietnam Veteran. Through his art he helps improve the spirits of military families who find solace in the beauty of his work and in the dignified compassion he shows in remembrance of their loved ones. http://www.fallenheroesproject.org/

USO-Metro: Is a non-profit chartered by Congress and dedicated to "serving those who serve, and their families" in

Washington D.C., Maryland and N. Virginia. It is through the generous financial support of individuals and organizations in the local community that USO-Metro is able to full its mission. With the help of thousands of devoted volunteers, USO-Metro provides programs and services for active duty troops and their families at area military hospitals, six USO Centers, four USO airport lounges and Mobile USO. Signature programs and services include holiday programs like **Turkeys for Troops** and **Project USO Elf**, emergency housing and food assistance, and caring for our wounded, ill and injured troops and their caregivers. www.us.uso.org/washingtonbaltimore/

WEST VIRGINIA:

MilitaryConnection.org: Is a great resource tool providing a variety of resources for various needs for the W.V military community.

Free Glasses: All active duty military, guard and reservists on active duty more than 30 days, and retired military may be eligible for free glasses and sunglasses.
http://www.med.navy.mil/sites/nostra/order/Pages/Eligibility.aspx

WV ASPEN: This site includes resources available to help with whatever difficult problem or situation you are facing containing supportive services that will aid you in your journey to help, hope, and healing.
http://www.wvaspen.com/help/veterans-military.html

WISCONSIN:

Being There Reaching Out Inc: Provides assistance to families of the Wisconsin men and women lost in, or due to our nation's wars. Their mission is to be there for them emotionally, physically and economically. And to reach out to them by organizing primarily private gatherings which allow them to heal through one-on-one communication and sharing with one another. http://www.beingtherereachingout.org/

Tax Credit for Wisconsin Vets: The WI-Vets & Surviving Spouses Property Tax Credit provides eligible veterans and un-remarried surviving spouses a refundable property tax credit for their primary in-state residence. The WDVA verifies the veterans' eligibility for the program and the credit is administered by the WI-Dept. of revenue through the state income tax return. For more information, go to the Wisconsin Department of Veteran Affairs website or contact your county veterans service officer. http://dva.state.wi.us/Ben-taxbenefits.asp and http://www.veteransunited.com/futurehomeowners/veteran-property-tax-exemptions-by-state/

Vets Journey Home (VJH): Is an all-volunteer organization that helps with the emotional healing of service members. VJH started in 1989 as Bamboo Bridge to work on the emotional healing of Viet Nam Vets. In 2004 the name was changed to include all active duty, reserve and veterans, all service times and all branches of service. All retreats are FREE to service members. They are located in Wisconsin, Maryland, Pennsylvania, Florida, Texas and California. The volunteers are veterans and civilian family members of vets, reserves, or active duty. The weekend retreats are put on to assist participants with unloading the emotional baggage they carry due to experiences in service to our country. www.vetsjourneyhome.org

WYOMING:

Honoring Our Veterans Program: Therapy programs for OEF/OIF combat wounded veterans offered in Wyoming are a part of the "Honoring Our Veterans Program." They offer weeklong recreational therapy session to post 9/11 combat wounded veterans. Honoring Our Veterans mission is to improve the quality of life for post 9/11 combat wounded veterans by offering them activities that strengthen their physical, cognitive, emotional, and social functioning. The programs are offered in Jackson Hole, Wyoming and there is no cost to the wounded veteran. The program covers the travel, activity, lodging, and food expenses.

The sessions include, water sports, fly-fishing, and woodcarving and they have seven spots open per session. All our wounded veterans stay together in condominium units and stay together at all times. Each wounded veteran is asked to share a room with another warrior. In addition to the participating wounded veterans, they also provide two aides on hand at all times. Effort is made to ensure each wounded veterans is comfortable and has what they need in order to facilitate the most relaxed healing experience. Correspondence is made with the veterans before the session starts in order to decrease their anxiety and answer any questions or concerns they might have. Here is a copy of a newsletter and previous photos of sessions. http://www.honorvets.org/newsletters.html; they also have images and videos from previous sessions online: http://www.honorvets.org/photos-videos.html POC is Sandra Budak, Executive Director Home office: (307) 543-2135 Cell phone: (307) 713-5678 sandrabudak@honorvets.org

State Resources

Michigan Food & Farming Systems (MIFFS) is dedicated to supporting the many faces of farming, particularly our beginning and historically underserved farmers. These farmers grow diversified crops and raise animals, they live in rural and urban areas, and they farm individually, in groups, on incubator farms, and as cooperatives.

As a statewide, membership-based nonprofit organization, MIFFS has been connecting farmers to resources and opportunities since 1998. We honor each farmer's passion for working the land and growing the food, while also recognizing that they can and must do it in a way that is viable and sustainable for the earth and for their pocketbooks.

We invite you to Rise Up and Dig In! Read about our programs, our events and our farmers, as well as join our membership, donate, volunteer or find out how you can participate in our activities.

With your support, we will continue building a food system that is stronger and healthier for our families and communities, based on fair prices, established through local relationships, and committed to environmentally-friendly practices.

WEB:MIFFS.org   Email: miffs@msu.edu
FACEBOOK: https://www.facebook.com/MIVetsInAg
Phone: 517-432-0712

MICHIGAN MILITARY RESOURCES

Each state has their own resources to help facilitate assistance for it's community. Since I live in Michigan, it only makes sense to list more resources from this state. I am proud to say Michigan's community has stepped up in amazing ways in all areas of need for its Military Community and it gets stronger each year.

Army Community Service (ACS): ACS is located in U.S. Army Garrison – Detroit Arsenal, Building 232 (Adjacent to the Visitor's Center), 6501 E. Eleven Mile Road, Warren, MI 48397. Service members (all U.S. military branches of service), military retirees, DoD Civilians, the family members of the groups mentioned before, Families of the Fallen, Families of POWs, Families of MIA Service Members are eligible for ACS services. Information related to family services, which are needed by eligible people (see above to view eligibility of clients)

Family advocacy * Preventive education courses * Financial matters * Deployment assistance * Relocation services (when you must move) * Family Readiness Group assistance * Volunteerism * Rear Detachment Commands assistance * Family team building * Sexual assault issues * Resume assistance * Domestic violence liaison * Job search assistance * Survivor Outreach Services * New parent support *

Survivor Outreach Services and more. Please call for further details 586-282-0489, visit www.detroitarseanlfmwr.com (click on "ACS"), or watch ACS' YouTube videos which have a wealth of information. Search "Detroit Arsenal ACS" or "ACS2826960Outreach".
http://myarmybenefits.us.army.mil/Home.html

Camp Liberty, Inc.: Camp Liberty is a 501 (c) (3) non-profit organization that features over a 135 acres of beautiful Michigan woods, fields, wetlands, and ponds teaming with wildlife. Camp Liberty will provide an exceptional setting for the whole family to enjoy the natural therapeutic experience unique to inclusive recreation together in the great Michigan outdoors. It provides programs designed to aid in the rehabilitation and reintegration of U.S. Military service members, veterans, their families, and other individuals that may be facing health challenges. Camp Liberty programs rely on an all-volunteer workforce, donations, sponsors, grants, and people like you. For more information call (810) 908-1901 or visit www.camp-liberty.org.

Cherry Street Health Services: FREE individual Financial Empowerment sessions for veterans and their families. If anyone in the military is interested in having a one-on-one time with an advisor to learn about savings for emergencies, making a household budget, applying for benefits (including food assistance, emergency relief, childcare assistance, Medicaid, healthy Michigan Plans, and purchasing Insurance through the marketplace for family members who are not covered through the VA), dealing with debt, understanding your credit score and more! All sessions are by appointment only and will be held at 201 Sheldon Blvd SE Grand rapids, MI 49503. If interested contact Tamara Landon (616) 965-8282 EXT 7199/ tamaralandon@cherryhealth.com

Combat Veterans Program: The John Dingell VA Medical Center has a team of providers who specialize in the assessment and treatment of Post-Traumatic Stress Disorder

(PTSD). The mission of the PTSD Clinic Team (PCT) is to provide comprehensive, individuated, and state-of-the-art treatment for veterans who have been impacted by traumatic events that occurred during military service. The program provides assessment for PTSD, education, group and individual therapy, and assistance with connecting to other needed services. If you believe you or your family member would benefit from these services, please contact the PCT at (313) 576-1000 EXT 65770. Or PCT Coordinator, Christina Hall, LMSW (313) 576-4962.

Community Provider ToolKit: Offers many resources to assist organization that support veterans in many areas of their lives. To do this, they provide a brief Resource Plan that you can complete with your client to assess potential needs and match resources. They have included contact information on many of the services listed below on the resource plan itself so that it can be used as a quick reference tool. See more at: http://www.mentalhealth.va.gov/communityproviders

Detroit Vet Center #402: Is a Veterans Readjustment Counseling Center for Women that Provides assistance in area of Military Sexual Trauma. Phone: (313) 831-6509

Disability Compensation: (800) 827-1000
http://www.benefits.va.gov/compensation.

Disabled Sports USA (DS/USA) – Great Lakes Adaptive Sports Association (GLASA): Offers sports rehabilitation programs, including winter skiing, aquatic sports, competition and special sports events, to anyone with a permanent disability. Learn about the Disabled Sports USA Warfighter Sports program that serves wounded warriors, including those injured in the Iraq and Afghanistan wars, through sports rehabilitation programs in military hospitals and communities across the U.S.
http://glasa.org/

Educational Assistance: (888) 442-4551 http://gibill.va.gov/

Free Veteran Legal Clinic: If you are having issues with the VA, need some legal help with all the VA paperwork? The University of Detroit-Mercy offers free legal services for veterans as part of their Project Salute. For more information contact U of D-M at (888) 836-5294 or visit the website at http://www.law.udmercy.edu/index.php/projectsalute.

Goodwill Industries – Mid-Michigan: Their mission is to help individuals become self-reliant and independent. Services can include, but not limited to referrals for Work Assessment/ Adjustment, Life Skills, Employment, Training, access to computer labs, accommodations information, community access, referral, small business development, and individual counseling for issues affecting employment and training. In addition, job ready candidates may utilize good temps, Goodwill's temp-to-perm staffing solution. Goodwill is a flexible agency attempting to provide services responding to changing personal and economic needs. www.goodwill.org

Gulf War Veteran Information: (800) 827-1000
http://wwwpublichealth.va.gov/exposures/gulfwar/

Health Care Information: (877) 222-8387
http://va.gov/health/default.asp

Hearing Impaired: (800) 829-4833

Helping Our Heroes: POC: Leslie Melvin (517) 974-0987
http://www.helpingourheroesmichigan.org/

Homeless Assistance – Degage Ministries: Offers programs to meet immediate needs for veterans in crisis or transition. Also helps the homeless navigate obstacles and work toward housing, jobs, sobriety, health, and independence. www.degageministries.org

Home Buying Assistance: (800) 827-1000
http://benefits.va.gov/homeloans/

Homeless PACT (Patient Aligned Care Team): (Detroit) Is part of the John D. Dingell Medical Centers Homeless Veterans Program, and is part of a nationwide project of DoVA; designed to identify homeless veterans in the community through outreach activities. The program offers accessible, comprehensive care coordinated by a team that establishes a continuity relationship with the veteran. Services provided: * Medication Management & review *Substance Abuse, Addiction Therapy * Psychiatric Treatment * Vaccinations * Women's Healthcare * Community Outreach Healthcare * Consulting to specific services in eye clinic, audiology, ENT – Ear/Nose/Throat clinic, Prosthetics and much more. (313) 576-1580, Address: 301 Piquette St, Detroit 48202. M-F 8:00 A.M. – 4:00 P.M. www.va.gov/homeless/h_pact.asp

Homeless Veterans Reintegration Program: (Grand Rapids Area) Provides employment training and job search assistance for Veterans who do not have secure and permanent housing. For more information call: (616) 437-1851 or (616) 292-6592.

Hospice of Helping Hands: Is a proud partner with the *We Honor Veterans Program*, and holds a partner level four recognition. This recognition ensures that their hospice employees are specially trained to care for and accommodate veteran patients through a partnership with the National Hospice and Palliative Care Organization and Veteran's Administration. How this is provided: Continued veteran specific hospice education for hospice staff in order to provide tailored care for veterans * Veteran-to-veteran volunteer program * Obtaining a military history checklist at admission * Flag draping at death * Annually in November they conduct over a dozen "We honor veterans celebrations service", hosting a veterans resource open house, and a free screening of the film Honor Flight. www.hohh.org (800) 992-6592

Life Insurance: (800) 669-8477
http://www.benefits.va.gov/insurance

Make the Connection: Is a national, public awareness campaign by the Department of Veteran Affairs that features candid, personal testimonials from veterans and their loved ones and provides access to local resources. Take a look at the Gallery for short videos from real veterans.
http://maketheconnection.net/

Minority Veterans Information: (800) 827-1000
http://www.va.gov/CENTERFORMINORITYVETERANS

Military Mom: Is comprised primary of military moms who meet monthly to support each other, their military children and our US troops in general. Military Moms is not political and was first organized by a small group of moms at the start of the Iraq war. The group has steadily increased and currently has over 100+ members. If you wish to attend a meeting or learning more you can email: info@militarymomsmm.com or visit website at http://militarymomsmm.com/

Michigan Public Service Commission: Will provide Utility Help For Military Families—Protection includes a period of 90 days shut-off protection Shut off protection for at least one additional 90-day period as long as the family continues to meet all of the conditions for an eligible military family and A payment schedule at the close of the 90 days that allows the customer to pay past due bills in monthly installments over a 12-month period. Eligible military family includes a utility customer, spouse of a customer, or customer whose spouse is in the military who meets all of the following: Is on full-time active duty * Is deployed overseas in response to a declared war or undeclared hostilities or is deployed within the U.S. in response to a declared national or state emergency with a reduction in household income. Applicant needs to provide verification of eligibility by contacting (800) 292-9555.

Michigan State University: Vets to Ag Program is a 6 week program administered by Tom Smith, and is a unique program to train homeless US veterans to work in agriculture. Training is coordinated by the MSU Institute of Agricultural Technology and is delivered by experts from MSU faculty and staff, including MSU Extension, Kellogg Biological Station, and the private sector.

Training includes: Basic plant and soil science; Equipment and workplace safety; Equipment Operation; Computer skills; Integrated pest soil science; Equipment and workplace safety; Equipment operation; Computer skills; Integrated pest management; Training for the Michigan certified pesticide applicator exam; and Specific training in a broad range of agricultural industries. For more information go to http://iat.msu.edu/iat/vets_to_ag.

Michigan Hardest Hit Program: Is a program designed to prevent foreclosures. The Helping Hardest Hit Homeowners Program consists of three options which will assist homeowners to avoid foreclosures. https://www.stepforwardmichigan.org/ and http://www.michigan.gov/mshda/

Unemployment Mortgage Subsidy Program: Is meant to provide homeowners currently receiving unemployment benefits funding to ensure that mortgage payments are made to avoid foreclosures. The program will help homeowners stay current with their mortgages by funding 59% (up to $750) of their monthly mortgage payments. Homeowners will continue to be responsible for the remaining 50% of their payments. The subsidy is available for up to 12 consecutive months, or until the homeowner has returned to work, whichever is less. http://www.freddiemac.com/singlefamily/service/hfa_relief.html and/or http://www.michigan.gov/documents/mshda/Unemployment_Mortgage_Pmt_Subsidy_Specs_6-10_325658_7.pdf

Michigan Resources

Loan Rescue Program: Many homeowners may experience a temporary financial hardship such as unemployment, divorce, or illness. When these situations cause a homeowner to miss mortgage payments, it is often difficult to get back on the right track. The new Loan Rescue Program was created to provide funding to homeowners who have recovered from a one-time crisis, but remain on the brink of foreclosure. The program will provide up to $5,000 to homeowners who can now afford to cover their current monthly payments, but need help to catch up on past due payments or delinquent taxes. https://www.stepforwardmichigan.org/ and http://www.nolo.com/legal-encyclopedia/michigans-hardest-hit-funds-program.html

Principal Curtailment Program: Provides up to $10,000 to underemployment homeowners with severe negative equity in their homes. Under this program, the mortgage servicer must agree to match the funding given by the State to reduce the principle balance; thereby creating more affordable housing payments for the homeowner. Eligible Michigan homeowners can also apply directly at www.stepforwardmichigan.org or call (866) 946-7432/(517) 373-1058 and speak with Nancy Baker, Business Development Specialist Homeowners Division bakern1@michigan.gov

Michigan Veterans Homeowners Assistance Program (MiVHAP): Assists service members and veterans with funding assistance to prevent foreclosure. Michigan military service members and veterans struggling to keep their homes because of mortgage foreclosure crisis could be eligible for financial assistance from the state. Attorney General Bill Schuette and the Director of the Michigan Veterans Affairs Agency, Jeff Barnes announced $5 million is available to assist military service members and veterans who are losing or have already lost their homes to foreclosure since 2006. Eligible Michigan residents include active and reserve military service members, Air and National Guard, honorably discharged veterans and surviving spouses of Michigan service members who had a combated-related death. The grants will be granted on a first-come, first-served basis until the money runs out. www.michigan.gov/dmva/

MiVetLaw.com (Michigan Veteran's Law): Provides (military discount and Free Consultations) legal assistance in the areas of * Security Clearance Appeals * Landlord Tenant Cases * Division of Retired Pay * Employment Rights * Military Divorce * Custody and Support * VA Benefits Appeals Contact Thomas J. Hetchler Jr. (517) 908-3480/(866) 988-4662 Help@MiVetLaw.com

Michigan Veteran Trust Fund: Is a state funded, emergency financial grant program. This grant is administered through your county level Trust Fund committees and applications for a MVTF grant are taken in the county of your residence home by authorized agents of the Michigan Veterans Trust Fund. Contact your local office for eligibility requirements and an application. Local veterans of Ingham County can contact the following:

Ingham County Department of Veteran Affairs
5303 S. Cedar
Lansing, MI 48911
(517) 887-4331

Michigan Warrior Hockey: A non-profit organization partnered with the Michigan Amateur Hockey Association giving our disabled Veterans the ability to get back on the ice by providing free ice time, assistance with equipment and most importantly an educational, competitive and supportive atmosphere for those of all skill levels. For more information regarding the program contact Joshua Krajewski at MichiganWarriorsHockey@gamil.com You can follow the team at www.facebook.com/MichiganWarriorsHockey

National Resource Directory for Veterans: They are encouraging all Veteran Service Providers to register in the

National Resource Directory. https://www.ebenefits.va.gov/ ebenefits/nrd/suggest-resource

No Veteran Left Behind: Is a resource organization designed to assist U.S. military veterans with any/all needs to adapt back into civilian society. *After evaluations, match veterans with any mental, health, or social work professional needed (if necessary). * Will assist in obtaining legal counsel for veteran or civilian needs * Will refer veterans to a substance abuse rehabilitation facility (in-patient or out-patient) * Will assist military veterans with job skills (based on assessment), resume building, interviewing skills and referrals * Will help with financial management and tax preparation upon securing employment * Will assist in transportation and clothing needs upon receiving employment (proof of employment required) * Will assist in finding reasonable housing both transitional and long term (may be subject to income requirements). www.noveteranleftbehind.us (313) 595-1262 or (313) 978-4443 veteranrescue@gmx.com

Our Home Transitional: Provides assistance to homeless single female veterans including job training and placement, educational training, home placement assistance and mental and physical healthcare. www.endlesscrowds.com

Plachuta, Murphy & Associates' Veterans Scholarships: Provides the military community discount assistance for any legal assistance they made need. Also provided are two Veteran Education Scholarship awards in the amount of $500 each to veterans attending a Michigan College or University. Deadline in July 31st each year. For eligibility requirments for scholarship and question for legal assistance contact www.pmalawpc.com

Point Man International Ministries – Michigan: This is a national organization/non-profit doing supportive work in U.S.A and is run by veterans from all eras, nationalities and background helping military members, veterans and their families. Although, the primary focus has always been to offer spiritual healing from PTSD; they have evolved in group meetings, publishing, hospital visits, conferences, supplying public speakers for churches and veterans groups, welcome home projects and community support. Just about anywhere there are Vets, there is a Point Man presence offered by Point Man are FREE OF CHARGE. www.pmim.org

Project Healing Waters: The John Dingell VA Hospital is teaming up with Project Healing Waters to teach veterans the art of Fly Fishing in room B1290, See website for dates and times or contact Kelly Cousion at (313) 576-1217.

Program Scope: The Michigan Attorney General targeted funds from the National Mortgage Settlement to assist Military service members and veterans with issues related to the foreclosure crisis.

The Michigan Veterans Trust Fund state office state members will administer funding assistance to prevent foreclosure. Grants are subject to approval based on program criteria. The MIVHAP will provide financial grant assistance to Active military service members; Reserve, Air and Army National Guard, and honorably discharged veterans living or having lived in a home in Michigan.

The MiVHAP may assist with residual effects related to the foreclosures crisis, since 2006. Eligible surviving spouses of military service members, whose deaths have been deemed to be combat related since 2006, may also be provided financial assistance.

Point of Contact
Erik Napieralski MI Veterans Trust Fund – MiVHAP
P.O. Box 30104
Lansing, Mi 48909
Phone: 517-284-5296
Fax: 517-284-5297

Social Security Benefits for Wounded Veterans: Disabled veterans who are receiving benefits from the VA, may be entitled to extra benefits from Social Security Administration.

In many cases veterans prior to 1967 did not get full credit for their services with the Social Security Administration. If they are retiring they need to take a copy of their DD-214 to the SSA office. If already retired take a copy of their discharged papers to the SSA to get earnings record corrected. This may increase financials per month. For more information go to http://www.socialsecurity.gov/woundedwarriors/

Tight Lines for Troops: Mission is to unite organizations, businesses, sponsors and communities to help provide a **free** fishing tournament open to all Michigan veterans from all eras, wartime and peacetime. By bringing our Heroes together, the goal is to build and foster new relationships, share experiences and enjoy fishing in the great outdoors of Michigan. Their all-volunteer, not-for-profit efforts improve the quality of life for many veterans, reinforce patriotism, educate and bring awareness that continue to support and honor those who have defended our country and our freedoms. For more information about the Tight Lines for Troops Sponsorship form or to participate in other opportunities to help, please contact Bob Guenthardt at (231) 723-3282 or renegade22@att.net.

The Trauma Healing Project: An Integrated, Innovative, Holistic Method for Treating PTSD works to heal the whole person, not just treating symptoms, treats the family as a unit since they are all affected, Uses simple methods which can be learned and practiced at home, or anywhere at any time, No Drugs which only mask the pain and True healing from the trauma. Holistic Methods for Treatment Include: Auricular Acupuncture, Emotional Freedom techniques, Hypnosis, EMDR, Negative Affect Erasing Method, Power to Peace Stress Elimination, Healing Codes technology and Nutritional Counseling. For more information, referrals or appointments call (517) 887-0843 EMAIL: HealingTrauma@msn.com. www.healingattention.org

VA funds to subsidize permanent and supportive housing to vets in need: VA will be offering additional funds to subsidize permanent and supportive housing to vets in need... The chart link below shows Michigan will get 230 vouchers to be administered through the listed agencies... please pass the word to vets who could be helped by this program. https://portal.hud.gov/hudportal/documents/huddoc?id=HUDVASH2013R1FundChart.pdf

Veteran Crisis Line (800) 273-8255: the professionals at the Veteran Crisis Line are specially trained and experienced in helping veterans of all ages and circumstances. Many of the responders are veterans themselves and understand what veterans and their families and friends have been through and the challenges veterans of all ages and service eras face. http://veteranscrisisline.net/

Veteran Employment (Southfield): The State of Michigan has an employment specialist located in Southfield at the John Grace Center, 21030 Indian St. His primary function is to assist Southfield veterans in finding a job. Contact Mr. Mark Meadows at (248) 796-4569 or email meadowsm@michigan.gov

Veterans Haven Inc: Veterans Haven provides housing, food, clothing, medical supplies and medical equipment, education and employment resources. Help for Michigan disabled veterans (including those with developmental disabilities and mental illness) with shelters, housing and more. http://www.vetshaveninfo.org/ POC: 4924 S. Wayne Rd. Wayne, MI 48184. (734) 728-0527. EMAIL: vetshaven@gmail.com

Veterans Hiring Guide: This guide includes Key benefits for hiring veterans, Jobs for which many veterans would qualify, Understanding military training and ranks Core values, abilities and typical duties. For additional information visit www.talent2025.org

Veteran Housing Project: Assists disabled and/or low income veterans who need assistance maintaining and cutting the weeds in their yard, fixing a leaking sink, need a wheelchair ramp installed, etc.. The Oakland County chapter of the Rebuilding Together Program may be able to help. The volunteers go to the veteran's house, cut your weeds, fix that leak, and build wheelchair ramps and much more. Contact Mr. Jerry McKay (248) 889-5450 http://www.veteranshousingproject.org/

Veteran Round Table: Strives to link both Disabled Owned Business and Veteran Owned Business to contracting opportunities with major corporations in commercial markets and with federal, state and local governments in the public sector. The Roundtable interacts with oficals in governments of all levels and engages corporate management to advocate for the interests of SDVOB and VOB. The Roundtable works for access, legitimacy and growth for veteran owned business of all sizes and types. Through matchmaking veteran outreach activities and other networking events the Roundtable endeavors to educate, facilitate and encourage the prosperity of veterans and their families in the free markets for which they have stood in vigilant defense. For more information and contact information at www.veteranroundtable.org

Veteran Task Force of the SE Michigan Synod of the Evangelical Lutheran Church in America: Is a growing network of community agencies, houses of faith, caring individuals and members of the military working & praying together to respond to the needs of returning troops, veterans and their families.

The V.T.F. goals are to mobilize local faith centers and communities to provide assistance to returning troops and their families as they transition from combat duty to civilian life. For more information contact Rev. Carl Ames at (734) 722-1735 and/or pastorames@sbcglobal.net LOCATION: Prince of Peace Lutheran Church – 37775 Palmer Rd, Westland, MI 48186.

Veteran Services: If you are a veteran seeking employment (Grand Rapids area) or an employer seeking qualified veterans for your open positions contact (616) 532-4200 or email veteranservices@goodwillgr.org

Veteran Transitional Housing Program: (Grand Rapids) Offers up to two years of transitional housing and support to veterans who enter the program homeless. This program helps veterans learn the skills needed for long-term stability and helps veterans secure employment and permanent housing. For more information, call (616) 366-1340 or (616) 890-6852.

Veterans Workforce Investment Program: (Grand Rapids) addresses the unique needs of Veterans seeking employment. Goodwill assists eligible veterans in a variety of areas relating to job training, placement and retention with an emphasis on green career fields. Veterans also receive support in developing and strengthening employability skills. For more information contact Kent County: (616) 893-2335 or (616) 318-1965. Clare, Gladwin, Ionia, Isabella, Mecosta, Montcalm and Osceola Counties (231) 206-0127.

VFW Camp Trotter for Military Children: Where nature and patriotism meet for children 7-12 year olds. The camp includes summer activities on site such as swimming, boating, hiking, biking, arts and crafts, archery, softball, volleyball as well as campfire activities. The children are given a general knowledge of science, art, nature and are taught patriotism, courage, self-reliance and kindred virtues. Volunteers/ Members strive to further instill upon the campers morals and values by combining educational activities with fun. Their goal is to guide and assist our youth to build a more conscientious, responsible, and productive society. For Camp Trotter application download it from the website at http://www.vfwcamptrotterfoundation.org/home.aspx Camp Trotter is located in Newaygo, Mi (231) 652-7241

VISN 11 Telehealth: Uses health informatics, diseases management and Telehealth technologies to target care and case management to improve access to care, improving the health of veterans. Call Casey Thayer, facility Telehealth Coordinator for more information about the program at (269) 966-5600 EXT 36234 Casey.Thayer2@va.gov

Vocational Rehabilitation and Employment: (800) 827-1000 http://www.va.gov/ and follow links.

Wilwin Lodge-Trout Lake, Michigan: It is located in the Eastern Upper Peninsula. The American Legion Department of Michigan owns the WilWin Lodge and uses the property to offer soldiers returning from Iraq or Afghanistan a secluded place to reconnect with their families. It is open from May 1st to November 1st each year. Veterans anywhere in the country can book time at Wilwin by filling out and submitting the application on its website. For additional information visit www.wilwin.org click on "Contacts" tab, download the application and follow instructions.

Women Veterans Issues: (800) 827-1000 http://www.womenshealth.va.gov/

World War II Re-enacted on Lake Michigan (General): To see the momentous events of WWII come alive, be sure to visit southwest Michigan at beginning of June. The cities of Benton Harbor and St. Joseph are hosting a public event called **Lest We Forget.** Its motto: "We brighten the future by illuminating the past." Tiscornia Beach and Southwest Michigan Regional Airport are the scenes of events. Activities include: beach landings, ground battles, classic vehicle and equipment displays, beach craft exhibits, airplane and helicopter rides, flyovers, demonstrations, parachute jumps, Medal of Honor speakers, a vehicle parade, Big Band entertainment and plenty of chow. The stars of the show are some 440 re-enactors directed by the WWII Historical Re-enactor's Society. For details and the schedule of events, visit www.lestweforgetusa.org or call (269) 925-7176. Additional tourist information is available from the Southwestern Michigan Tourist Council.

MEDICAL CENTERS/HEALTHCARE SYSTEM

Aleda E. Lutz VA Medical Center
Website: www.saginaw.va.gov
Eligibility Office: (989) 497-2500 EXT 13120 or 13124
Toll-free (800) 406-5143 same extensions

Battle Creek VA Medical Center
Website: www.battlecreek.va.gov
Eligibility Office: (269) 966-5600 EXT 33887 or 33853
Toll-free (888) 214-1247

John D. Dingell VA Medical Center
Website: www.detroit.va.gov
Eligibility Office: (313) 576-1000 EXT 65731 or 64141
Toll-free: (511) 800-8056

Richard L. Roudebush VA Medical Center
Website: www.indianapolis.va.gov
Eligibility Office: (317) 554-000 EXT 84297
Toll-free: (888) 878-6889

VA Ann Arbor Healthcare System
Website: www.annarbor.va.gov
Eligibility Office: (734) 845-5274
Toll-free: (800) 361-8387

VA Illiana Health Care System
Website: www.danville.va.gov
Eligibility Office: (217) 554-3000 EXT 45369
Toll-free: (800) 320-8387

VA Northern Indiana Healthcare System
Website: www.northernindiana.va.gov
Fort Wayne Eligibility Office: (260) 426-5431 EXT 71101
Toll-free: (800) 360-8387
Marion Eligibility Office: (765) 674-3321
Toll-free (800) 360-8387

SCHOLORSHIPS/INTERNSHIPS

Old Warrior Camp: For returning vets who need some time to unwind and relax? In the Upper Peninsula of Michigan there is a camp where fishing hunting, riding, etc.are available for FREE. For more information go to
http://www.oldwarriorcamp.com
or EMAIL: thebuildogblevins@yahoo.com

Wounded Veteran Internship Program: Wounded veterans who cannot return to their previous civilian jobs after serving in combat can find placement opportunities with the Michigan Department of Transportation (MDOT) through a grant provided by the Federal Highway Administration. This program is being implemented to meet the employment needs of returning wounded veterans of the Armed Forces as they transition into the civilian workforce.
www.michigan.gov/woundedvetintern

Opportunities to work—learn—Earn * Placement depends upon the veteran's knowledge, skills and abilities. Possible fields include aeronautics, engineering, finance, maintenance, planning, project management and research. Please contact Bruce Freimark, Wounded Veterans Program Coordinator (517) 373-1532, freimarkb@michigan.gov

The Dept. of Licensing & Regulatory Affairs has prepared a compilation of services that may apply to Michigan's veterans, active military and military families. These services include occupational or business licensing, construction, workplace safety and health, unemployment, and utility assistance. http://michigan.gov/lara/0,4601,7-154-10573_68470---,00.html

West Michigan Veterans Coalition –

Prosperity Region 4 Veterans Community Action Team

About

The West Michigan Veterans Coalition is a community integrated system offering support services, resources, and programs to veterans and their families. Our role is to offer a comprehensive network of service providers, empowered with knowledge, information, and tools to effectively connect veterans to the appropriate resources to help facilitate assistance in education, employment, healthcare, and quality of life.

In 2013, the West Michigan Veterans Coalition was selected by the Michigan Veterans Affairs Agency to implement Altarum Institute's no-wrong-door collaborative Veteran Community Action Team (VCAT). The model is designed to enhance the delivery of services from public, private, and nonprofit organizations to veterans and their family members.

The VCAT aims to institute a community-based veterans' system of care through the establishment of broad-based coalitions of veterans' service organizations, health and community service providers, veterans and their family members, and other stakeholders.

Mission

To improve the lives of veterans, their families, and anyone that served in the Armed Forces by connecting them to all available services and resources throughout West Michigan. www.westmichiganveterans.com

Point of Contact

Elena Bridges, Chairperson
616-401-2026
Elena.Bridges@altarum.org

HELPING OUR TROOPS
AND FAMILIES

American Legion's Comfort Warriors: Makes sure our veterans who are away from home and their families have the personal comfort items they need from home. www.legion.org/operationcomfortwarriors

The Boot Girls: Began the grassroots initiative to help returning American troops injured in combat. For every pair of military boots sold, a minimum of $25 goes to several groups assisting wounded Soldiers and their families. Their goal is to get 1.4 million Americans to purchase the boots – one for every active duty military person. http://www.bootcampaign.com/ ****I think this organization is really cool and I love how the celebrity community has jumped on board and shown their support in a unique and very interesting easy to accomplish way. My hats off to you ladies!**

Code of Support Foundation: The foundation works to engage and leverage the full spectrum of this nation's resources to ensure that our service members, veterans, and their families receive the support they need and have earned through their service and sacrifice. www.codeofsupport.org

Troops and Families

Hazlewood Act: U.S. District Judge Ewing Werlein JR, ordered the University of Houston not to exclude the plaintiff, Keith Harris, from benefits under the Texas Hazelwood Act solely because he enlisted in the Army while living outside Texas. The Hazelwood Act provides tuition and fee exemptions from state public universities for military veterans, their spouses and their children. The clause in question limits the benefits to veterans who were Texas residents when they enlisted, but Ewing found that this provision violates the equal protection clauses of the 14th Amendment to the US Constitution. The ruling could have broad implications for Texas schools, which bear most of the costs of the benefit.
http://www.michigan.gov/mshda/

Lots of Helping Hands: Connecting people through the power of community – whether you need help or you want to provide help. You may be caring for an ill loved one, an aging parent, a child with special needs or a veteran. You may want to volunteer to help a friend or others in your neighborhood. However you define help—this is your home.
www.lotshelpinghands.com

MANning the Homefront: Is a Facebook group and began in 2010, out of Fort Riley, Kansas. They are geared specifically toward male military spouses; and focus on connecting and support of the MANspouse; by doing this they are accomplishing the goal of supporting our female service members and their families. They believe the best way to support the married female service member is to support her family and to the best of their ability.

Though it started small this group focus has had enormous positive impact on military families as it engages MANspouses from every branch of service, providing community support, strength and integrity. The MANspouse Facebook page has helped grow the group throughout other installations, bridge thousands of miles and every branch of service. The group numbers to 50+ and is growing every day.

It's important to remember MANspouse doesn't try to be a support group, but more of a source of camaraderie for the few-and-far-between male military spouses. Female service members are encouraged to sign their husbands/fiancés/ boyfriends up and tell him he is going, or will receive a phone call as a follow up to see him they need anything.

MANspouse goal is to give the spouse a sense of his own community within the overall military community so he will become more actively involved in our military community just as female military spouses have been doing for ages. For more information about MANning the Homefront, call 864-304-4059, visit their Facebook page or email MANningTheHomefront@hotmail.com

Military & Veterans Appreciation Trust Foundation (MVAT): Raises funds for charities that support wounded warriors, service members, veterans and their families. http://www.mvat.org/beneficiaries

The Rosie Network: Is a non-profit founded by military spouses whose mission is to promote the entrepreneurial efforts of American veterans and military spouse business owners. The talents and skills of these men and women are brought to the American public by showcasing their products and services on The Rosie Network website. Consumers search a selected geographic area for businesses owned and operated by military spouses and veterans. www.TheRosieNetwork.org

Veteran Staffing Network: Has a mission to provide their clients with top-tier talent while simultaneously reducing veteran unemployment. They provide supportive services to prepare veterans and their spouses to become job ready. They have a wide spectrum of skills sets available to clients so they are not limited to one industry and can support client needs across business disciplines. www.veteranstaffingnetwork.org

Troops and Families

The 31Heroes Project: Organizes nationwide athletic events and teams to raise funds for programs that support families of service members killed in action. Also provides grants, logistical assistance, coaching and mentoring to help veterans and service members' transition to civilian life and meet their personal goals. http://www.31heroes.com/

Yellow Ribbon Reintegration Program – EvenPLUS: Enables community partners, vendors, staff, Reserve Component service members and their families to find and register for upcoming Yellow Ribbon Reintegration Program events. http://www.yellowribbonevents.org/

Index

M

O

U

notes: